TANTRA
THE SECRET POWER OF SEX

By

ARVIND & SHANTA KALE

JAICO PUBLISHING HOUSE
Mumbai • Delhi • Bangalore
Kolkata • Hyderabad • Chennai

TANTRA : THE SECRET POWER OF SEX
ISBN 81-7224-076-7

First Jaico Impression : 1976
Fourteenth Jaico Impression : 1998
Fifteenth Jaico Impression : 1999
Sixteenth Jaico Impression : 2000
Seventeenth Jaico Impression : 2001

Published by :
Jaico Publishing House
121, Mahatma Gandhi Road
Mumbai – 400 023.

Printed by:
Paras Printing Press
123, Adhyaru Ind. Estate.
Sunmill Compound,
Lower Parel,
Mumbai – 400 013.

CONTENTS

PART I
THE THEORY OF TANTRA

CHAPTER:

One: The Untapped Power of Sex 5

PART II
PREPARATION FOR TANTRA

Two: Your Tantric Partner 19

Three: Erotic Dress 34

Four: The Tantric Room 46

Five: Scent, Taste and Sex Hygiene 58

Six: The Sexual Muscles 69

Seven: Honing the Senses 79

PART III
THE TANTRIC JOURNEY

Eight: Sexual Awareness, the Duality Concept .. 93

Nine: Meditation for Sexuality 106

Ten: Stroking 118

Eleven: Floating 130

PART IV
SEXUAL POSITIONS

Twelve: Prolonged Sex 147

Thirteen: Positions for Variety 162

PART V
TANTRIC MORALITY

Fourteen: Tantra and Morality 177

CONTENTS

PART I
THE THEORY OF TANTRA

CHAPTER

One: The Untapped Power of Sex ... 5

PART II
PREPARATION FOR TANTRA

Two: Your Tantric Partner ... 19
Three: Erotic Dress ... 34
Four: The Tantric Room ... 46
Five: Scent, Taste and Sex Hygiene ... 58
Six: The Sexual Muscles ... 69
Seven: Honing the Senses ... 79

PART III
THE TANTRIC JOURNEY

Eight: Sexual Awareness, the Duality Concept ... 93
Nine: Meditation for Sexuality ... 100
Ten: Stroking ... 118
Eleven: Floating ... 130

PART IV
SEXUAL POSITIONS

Twelve: Prolonged Sex ... 147
Thirteen: Positions for Variety ... 162

PART V
TANTRIC MORALITY

Fourteen: Tantra and Morality ... 177

HOW TO USE THIS BOOK

This book is divided into five parts:

I **The Theory of Tantra**: A brief survey of the various explanations why Tantra works, with special emphasis on Tantric Sex.

II **Preparation for Tantra**: Advice on the equipment, exercises, mental approach, sexual partner, and other pre-requisites for your Tantric Journey.

III **The Tantric Journey**: Mental and disciplinary exercises needed to convert ordinary sex into Tantric Sex.

IV **Sexual Positions**: Positions to give variety to intercourse, and to help you prolong the act.

V **Tantric Morality**: A discussion on the reasons why Tantra and Tantrists contribute to the maturity, stabilisation and advancement of society.

For those who would like to speak with a certain, cocktail party, knowledge of Tantra, and have no other interest in the subject, Parts I and V will provide considerable background for superficial erudition.

For those who wish to improve their sex lives, but have no interest in Tantra, we recommend a reading of Parts II and IV.

For the sexual tyro, the seeker after pornographic thrills, the collector of erotica, this book has nothing to offer.

For that rare, sexually mature and experienced, couple who is genuinely interested in using sex to find out what lies beyond normal human experience....and who is not scared of failures and will-cracking discipline...the entire book has been written; they should, therefore, read the book from cover to cover and keep a record of their experiences. We have touched only the fringes of the subject in our attempt to make Tantra relevant to our age. We hope that a couple who reads this book will find the time to share their experiences with the world, as we have done.

ARVIND & SHANTA KALE.

Part I

THE THEORY OF TANTRA

Chapter One

The Untapped Power of Sex

This book is about sex. And the ecstasy of sex. And how you can use the ecstasy of sex to give you most of the things you want from life : success, good health, serenity and a 24-hour long sexual high.

It is not a new system. It is certainly as old as Hinduism which started 3500 years Before Christ. The Vedic Hindus had a very level-headed view of sex: it was an interesting subject and, therefore, they enquired into it with the same unswerving doggedness that they gave to mathematics, physics, phonetics and physical fitness. Thus, the people who gave the world the concept of the zero, atomic theory, the world's most phonetic alphabet and Hatha Yoga, also gave us the Science of Ecstasy. They called it Tantra.

Tantra and Yoga have much in common. Both are complete psycho-physical systems aimed at the perfection of the human being. Both use a number of varied sub-disciplines which provide a choice of paths to attain the objective: the monk chooses the path of Worship or Bhakti Yoga, the physically alert uses the path of Exercises or Hatha Yoga, and so on. Similarly, there are multiple, inter-connected paths afforded by Tantra: the path of sound, visualizations, mathematical patterns and sexual intercourse. In this book we shall deal with the sexual teachings of Tantra.

Sex in Tantra tries to heighten and prolong the special rapport that exists between a man and a woman when they are making love. In other words, the object of the sex act in Tantra is not the ecstatic pleasure of intercourse, but the 'oneness' that the man and woman experience when they are in such a sexual 'high'. The ecstasy is the means to the all-important 'oneness' end.

This state of Tantric 'oneness' is a mind-blowing experience. Time ceases to be, colours and sounds become intensely vivid, your sense of smell becomes animal-keen, your tongue savours subtle tastes you never knew existed and every inch of your hyper-sensitized skin sings with a whole new orchestration of feeling. But this incredible sensory flowering is only the beginning of your Tantric journey. The main dimension of the feeling lies in the knowledge....we use the word 'knowledge' because it is a certainty and not a mere feeling....the exploding awareness that all creation is one. For that timeless moment when you are held in the intoxication of a Tantric experience your consciousness flares to include everything around you: you **are** your neighbour, you **are** the wind in the pines, the bee in the flower, the planets in their courses, the galaxies streaming into space, the corpuscles in the blood of the person in your arms, the bright heart of an atom. For that burning instant the whole world stops and you alone are infinite and timeless.

It is impossible to describe this phenomenon; you have to live it to realise how inadequate our language is. For thousands of years eastern savants and yogis have tried to achieve this 'oneness' by meditation. Zen gives a glimpse of this rapture by the satori experience of a haiku poem: when you read the right haiku at the right time and in the right mood you will, for a heart-stopping moment, know the ecstatic unity of all creation. Other people have pursued this state through drugs, deprivation, even prayer. The spiritual exaltation of the Christian saints and the Muslim Sufi mystics was, undoubtedly, an experience of such bliss; a beatific vision, as the Christians called it. Saint Francis of Assissi sang of his satori experience in language which has been unrivalled in its simplicity and descriptive power: it also leaves no doubt about the vision of the gentle Italian.

Most of us, however, cannot understand the haiku, and we shy away from drugs, austere penances and intense prayer. Were it not for Tantra we would be permanently deprived of a whole dimension of living. But Tantra does exist and if you enjoy intercourse with a person of the other sex then you and your sexual partner should be able to share this intense experience.

Here, however, it is only fair to give you a word of warning. A mere repetition of the sexual act, in all its variations, is not Tantra. If this were so then Casanova would have been a great Tantric master. In actual fact Casanova and Don Juan and the other legendary lovers of the western world would have been held in the greatest contempt by the Tantrists of their age. To the Tantrist the west lays unreasonable emphasis on the quantity of sex: the more women a man copulates with the more heroic he becomes in the eyes of the society. Tantrists believe that such sexual performances are criminal wastes of the sexual powers. When the British first came to India and the soldiers began to boast of their sexual conquests, the bazaar prostitutes laughed at their claims and called them 'sparrows', trivial sexual creatures whose copulation was brief and meaningless. The symbol of Tantra is the erect phallus and one of the most rewarding disciplines of Tantra is that of maintaining the sexual tension between partners for prolonged periods: the staying power of a male Tantrist is seldom less than 3/4 of an hour, often it is considerably more than that. Much of the Tantric system is tailored to achieve this objective and some Tantrists contend that the male orgasm is an accident; if orgasm does occur the Tantric masters are said to have the ability to absorb their semen back into their bodies.

We do not claim to be able to teach you this siddhi, or power. Our claims are very modest. If you are able to master the basic disciplines we shall describe in the succeeding chapters then you will have only stepped over the threshold of Tantric experience. It might be possible to lead you a few more steps on the Tantric path by the method we have used here, but beyond that you will have to find your own guru to guide you. Like most eastern self-development disciplines, only the initial stages of Tantra can be taught through books; after that your instruction will have to be tailored to your individual needs and responses. This can only be done by an adept who knows you and has trod the Tantric path himself. We hope that many of our readers will seek and find such gurus; but we know that, for the majority, the

Tantric experience will be limited to the restricted path we have described here. This is an age of haste and few people believe that they have the time to search for the truth, even something so rewarding as the sexual truth.

To start with, therefore, we shall give you a capsule statement of Tantric theory, after which we shall try to be as practical as possible. In the chapters that follow we shall tell you what to do rather than why you should do it. But even if you are in a great hurry to get on with your Tantric development, we believe that you should know a little about the reasons behind the system. Or, to put it in another way, in the rest of this chapter we shall answer the question "Why does it work?" and in the rest of the book we shall answer the question "What must we do to make it work for us?"

A short answer to the first question is "It works because sex is the greatest driving force in the living world and Tantra uses that force." From there on, however, the answer splits into three distinct theories.

The biological explanation of Tantra argues that the human being is the only creature capable of copulating at all times because the adult human female is always on heat. This powerful incentive has given rise to a strange preoccupation with sex amongst humans; compared with other animals we are sex fiends totally obsessed with copulation. So great is the body's desire for sex that during copulation the digestion slows down and virtually stops, the cravings of hunger and thirst are dulled, the muscle tone improves, calories are burnt as rapidly as they are during a strenuous sprint, respiration and blood pressure increase pumping more oxygen and nourishment into the body, the senses become more sensitive, and the concentration is focussed with distraction—excluding intensity.

Or, to put it in another way, human beings are fittest during the act of love.

From these facts Tantrists reason that if the act of love could be prolonged in a controlled and disciplined way the partners in this extended state of fitness would reap a great harvest of good health. And it is a fact that the Tantric masters look incredibly youthful in spite of their advanced years; they certainly do not look like the debauchees their detractors make them out to be.

That is one theory. There is also a psychological explanation for the Tantric experience.

The mind is a triple-layered structure. Only the most superficial layer is subject to the will and, in evolutionary terms, it is the most recent development. The layer below is housed in a more primitive brain. Here lie the inhibitions, a buffer-state of a mind between the civilized, will-controlled, consciousness and the most ancient brain where the sub-conscious resides. And it is in this third, sub-conscious layer that all the extra-sensory powers seem to hide. It is from these dark well-springs that the poet draws his inspiration, the gambler his instinct, and the telepathist his strange contact with other minds. It would almost appear as if all human minds were linked by telepathic bonds, at this level, as close as the cells forming a single human body. Esoteric Tantric doctrine contends that this single Overmind is the repository of all mankind's memories and if anyone can make contact with it he will know the totality of mankind's experience and knowledge; the senses, thoughts and abilities of every man and woman who lives today, or has ever lived, will become his. But because this Overmind is a racial-mind, individuality cannot exist within it. It is only a single racial 'We' distinguished into the primal Male and Female. Tantrists believe that at the ego-dissolving moment before orgasm the minds of the partners make a fleeting contact with this Overmind. At that instant all Men are eternal uninhibited Male: Savage-Impregnating-Father-Rapist. And all Women at that moment are eternal Female: Lusting-Fecunding-Mother-Whore. And both are merged in self-perpetuating ecstasy where, in common with the goal of most great religions, the selfish 'I' is lost in the all-embracing 'We'. Tantra, therefore, seeks to use the rapture of sex to blast through the ego-protective barriers of our inhibitions and tap the incredible powers of this dark and omnipotent Overmind.

Finally, there is yet a third explanation for the ecstatic experience.

According to most Tantrists the theory that hews closest to the truth contends that all creation is a balance of opposites: light and dark, positive and negative, dynamic and kinetic. All these opposites can best be typified as Male and Female, symbolised as the Lingam, or penis in a state of erection, and the Yoni, or receptive vulva. The creation sustaining equilibrium of these opposing forces is symbolised by the Lingam in the Yoni during sexual intercourse. Tantra then believes that the sexual force can serve two purposes: the procreative and the creative. When used in its procreative role it is fulfilling a basic animal function: its species-preservation aspect. This same force can, however, be disciplined to serve a purely creative function and people who are naturally creative use this force instinctively. In support of this theory Tantrists point out that many western artists have blatantly unconventional sex lives. The reason for this, according to the Tantrists, is that their tapping of the sexual power is uncontrolled and, once the force is tapped, the artists do not know how to channel the power into a purely creative role. They also point out that driving sessions of creative work often leave the artist as limp and exhausted as if he had indulged excessively in sex, a markedly different exhaustion from that which overcomes a manual worker. This, they claim, is another manifestation of the indisciplined tapping of the sexual power.

Tantric theory holds that the creative power of sex lies curled, like a coiled serpent in the area between the anus and the generative organs. This creative power is known as the Kundalini. When the Kundalini can be made to rise up the body it will activate successive centres of creativity called Chakras. Finally, when it infuses and rises through the last Chakra at the top of the head, the knowledge of the unity of all creation will pour into the mind and there will be no distinction between the Created who seeks and the Reality who exists. This is the ultimate psychedelic experience, quite literally so, for when the Kundalini illumes the last Chakra you will see your Self, your Soul, for what it is: an indistinguishable part of the Great Soul that sustains, and is, Creation.

It will be seen that though these theories appear to be distinct and separate they are, in fact, merely three different ways of expressing the same concept. All creation is a balance of two opposing forces which we, human beings, can best appreciate as Male and Female. Our conscious minds are too limited to encompass this knowledge in its entirety. The only way in which we can realise this truth is through the intuitive faculties of our sub-conscious mind. To break through to this mind we have to use the driving power of sex because at the peak of sexual ecstasy the inhibitory barriers are pierced and contact is made with the uninhibited sub-conscious. Tantra seeks to prolong this contact, in a controlled and disciplined way, so that the door to the sub-conscious and thus to the knowledge of the duality of nature becomes part of our daily experience. This awareness of the oneness of all creation is an ecstatic experience in itself and may well be the beatific vision of the christian mystics.

At this stage you might well ask "If Tantra can achieve so much why isn't it better known? Why has it been kept hidden for so long?" The answer lies in the history of the Indian way of thought.

Much of Hindu belief has been influenced by the sexual ethic of the Muslim and Christian religions. While the orthodox Hinduism of today makes a virtue of aceticism, Tantra seeks illumination through the ecstasy of the senses. The five sacraments of Tantra are Meat, Fish, Grain, Wine and Sex. Tantra realises that pleasure can be a virtue if it can be disciplined: not the discipline of penalty and punishment, but rather the discipline of training and self-control. Far from renouncing pleasure, the Tantrist seeks to experience the most intense pleasure that can be tolerated and to maintain that ecstasy for as long as it can be held. Tantrists believe that their discipline is a positive one as distinct from the negative discipline of the ascetic. It is difficult to refute their contention.

Nevertheless, logical though the Tantrists reasoning may sound it is this pleasure-bias of Tantra that has brought it into disfavour in India. The Tantrist is viewed as a hedonist at best and a pervert and debauchee at worst. Reams have been written by well-meaning apologists seeking to high-light the symbolic aspects of Tantric sex rites and to play down the erotic elements: and this in a country where the sex act is depicted on the walls of the most revered shrines! As a result of this persecution Tantra went underground. Tantric sects held their meetings in secret, their scriptures were couched in a cryptic 'twilight language', their rites were never discussed openly.

Then, in the last ten years, western culture underwent a revolution: a surfeit of materialism caused the youth of the west to revolt against accepted values. They searched around for other ways to express themselves and they found it in psychedelic drugs, the security of the pill, the accessibility of fast travel and the sectarian-bridging challenges of universal problems: pollution, over-population, war. Suddenly this vast mass of affluent, searching, young people discovered a discipline that seemed to answer their unspoken needs. It was unconventional, inward-searching, mankind-oriented, and available to any couple who had the courage and determination to seek new ways of heightening their inter-personal relationships. After thousands of years of obscurity Tantra suddenly became fashionable again.

It was at this point that the reawakened interest in Tantra struck a major obstacle.

Tantra had remained a secret doctrine for so long that the entire lore had been bound up in symbolism, myth and allegory; and the symbols, myths and allegories had, themselves, been expressed as further emblems, fables and parables. The language of Tantra had become so allusive that it was virtually impossible for the student to discover the factual truth behind the multi-layered embroideries of imagery. Thus the secret doctrines of Tantra, of inestimable value to a troubled mankind, lay hidden under layer upon musty layer of philosophical discourse.

Nevertheless, in spite of the persecution, the light of Tantra still shone in all its pristine glory in some parts of India. In desert Rajasthan where feudal princes maintained the old practices in their guarded palaces, in a more sophisticated way in the delta lands of Bengal where the Great Mother has always been worshipped, but mostly in forested Assam where the Tantric savants fostered the ancient truths and passed them down carefully from **guru** to **chela.** But no wall is impregnable, no secret safe from the determined and dedicated seeker. Slowly, knowledge of the secret practices began to trickle out to the waiting world: old manuscripts were rediscovered, Tantric art was seen in a new light, the recorded words of ancient adepts began to acquire new meanings. Finally, the time was ripe to rephrase the great teachings in a language that could be understood by the modern world, to recast the ancient techniques and rituals so that they would be relevant today.

This is what we have attempted to do in this book.

We have sifted through the beautiful old rites to get to the truth around which they have been built. We have reconstructed the ceremonies in a modern setting so that today's man and woman will be able to relate to the truth without difficulty. In the regimen that we have worked out in the succeeding chapters we have started with the presumption that you are earnest about the subject. If you have bought this book believing it to be just another erotic treatise, you have made a mistake. There is certainly much to stimulate the senses and imagination in this book: that is the method of Tantra. But then those who seek sexual titillation can find it in the most unlikely places; there are people who find the Rorschach inkblots obscene. Not that you need go that far. There are a number of cheaper and more graphic books on the market which would serve your purpose better: you might even find some which claim to give you a course of Instant Tantra!

There is, of course, no short cut to the tapping of the sexual power. All that we have tried to do is to make the Tantric method easier for you to understand, but it still calls for a great deal of application and hard work, a certain amount of expense, and a complete overhauling of your mental attitude. For instance, it is not easy to prolong the sexual act and yet maintain sexual tension. In all likelihood you will fail many times and these failures will be extremely difficult to accept because we are conditioned by our society to be very sensitive about our sexual prowess. As for the expense, research is generally expensive and you are about to research into the nucleus of your Self. You will be particularly vulnerable during the initial period and we have devoted a whole chapter to the outfitting of the Sexual Room: the laboratory in which you and your partner will carry out most of your researches. Not everyone can afford to get all the 'equipment' we have suggested, and not everyone will need all of it, but if you can afford to invest in it you will achieve your results faster and with less effort. Finally, you will have to change your outlook on life. Tantra teaches the duality of all creation and you must train yourself to see this duality in the world around you. This is, perhaps, the most difficult of all the mental disciplines. The mind guards its climate with great jealousy, it detests change. You will have to combat these in-built prejudices, biases and habits which have now become an integral part of your personality, and replace them with new attitudes and new behaviour patterns. This does not mean, necessarily, that you will have to present a changed identity to the world. Tantra is not really concerned with your social image, but as your physical appearance is governed by the health of your internal organs, so too your social identity is a reflection of the climate of your mind. If your mental climate changes, as it must, then your social image is also likely to undergo a transformation, though it may not be very obvious at first.

These, then, are some of the methods we have used in this book to make Tantric practice relevant to our age, but because we have attempted to make an esoteric doctrine understandable to the lay person, we run the danger of being accused of having authored just another sexual primer. We find no way of avoiding this superficial charge. The ignorant might claim that Hatha Yoga is just another form of isometric exercise and there is no way of avoiding that accusation either. The sexual act has been written about **ad nauseum,** and men and women have only limited ways of making love. This book will, therefore, have to retrace certain well-trodden paths.

What is new, however, is the Tantric approach and that is:

  * That sexual pleasure is a means to an end;

* That the end is a spiritual ecstasy that is mind and personality expanding in its intensity;
* That such an experience can be had by every couple who practices Tantric sex;
* That the long term benefits of such sexual discipline is a virtual rejuvenation of the bodies and minds of the partners who experience such supra-sexual communion.

These are the promises of Tantra but please do not attempt Tantra unless you:

* Are a sexual sophisticate;
* Have a constant lover, not just a part-time attachment;
* Have the time, the will and resilience to bounce back from failures, particularly sexual failures:
* Are willing, if you are a man, to give up the western-oriented lets-hurry-to-an-orgasm goal.

These are essential qualifications and if you lack even one of them you are not ready for the Tantric adventure. Forget Tantra till you have reached sexual maturity. To attempt Tantra earlier would not only be frustrating, it might even, for some, be dangerous. You cannot afford to trifle with the power of Tantric sex.

But if you and your lover are mature, now is the time to start on the ecstatic path of Tantra.

Part II

PREPARATION FOR TANTRA

Chapter Two

Your Tantric Partner

Tantric sex is a tandem discipline: the unit is the couple and not the individual. It is the Tantric couple that explores the secrets of sexual ecstasy, no single person can do it alone. Being a tandem discipline the progress of the individual is linked to the success of the pair. It, therefore, follows that if you want to progress in the science of Tantra you will have to pick the right partner; in fact most of the Tantric savants were initiated by highly advanced Tantrists and the final stage of such initiation generally demands sexual intercourse with a high initiate.

But we do not intend to take you to these high levels of Tantra via this book; frankly, we doubt whether anyone can teach even middle-level Tantra through the written word. Our intention, as we have made clear earlier, is to introduce our readers to the initial ecstasies of Tantra because we believe that even such a limited knowledge of the science will result in great physical and mental wellbeing. If, then, our readers are interested in progressing further, we feel certain that they will be able to find a guru for themselves and learn the higher level of the science in the way it is expected to be taught: by personal example and instruction.

Nevertheless, even though our goals are limited, we wish to make it very clear to our readers that unless you and your Tantric partner are sexually mature, you run a grave risk if you attempt Tantra. It is, consequently, most important that you find the right partner before you tread the Tantric path.

To start with, mere physical maturity is not sexual maturity. Nowadays young people feel the stirrings of sex earlier than they used to. This is neither a good thing nor a bad thing in itself: it becomes a dangerous thing only because our society does not know how to handle it. Among the Maurias of Bastar, perhaps the most sexually enlightened people in the world, such early sexual maturity is no problem. Their children live in a communal compound called a **ghotul** and there they learn social graces, discipline, leadership and how to handle sex. It is a system that has worked so well that the Maurias were known for their complete absence of 'hang-ups', VD, marital infedility and sexual crimes. Regrettably we have to put all this in the past tense because recent reports that have come to our attention suggest that even this well-adjusted forest tribe is now falling a victim to modern 'civilization', and modern 'civilization' has nothing to offer its adolescents in lieu of the embattled **ghotul** system.

The success of the **ghotul** lies in the fact that it recognises that sexual physical maturity and sexual mental maturity do not occur at the same time: the first precedes the second by many years. A boy and a girl who may be physically capable of the sexual act might not be mentally able to handle the burden that society imposes on the act. We do not refer to the more obvious consequences of sexual intercourse such as VD and pregnancy, but to the importance attached by society to the act itself. Indian parents still advertise for 'virgin brides' for their sons, a wife's adultery is still a traumatic experience to the average Indian husband, sexual intercourse is still considered to be a sexual 'conquest.' Virginity, adultery and the possessive aspect of sexual intercourse are all part of the burden imposed by society on the sexual act: adolescents who are physically mature are just not mentally able to cope with this burden. They react by trying to downgrade the importance of sex which, in turn, only increases the gap between the physical cabability and the mental capacity to handle the 'hang-up' that such permissiveness creates.

The gap between physical and mental maturity is not restricted to adolescents: far from it. Adults are often more creatures of their milieu than adolescents are. Their sexual attitudes are frozen generally between the ages of 18 and 25, and these frozen attitudes, more often than not, reflect the attitudes of their families and social sub-groups with only superficial adaptations to meet current social trends. The junior executive and his wife might do their best to project a swinging Playboy Philosophy image, but in the secrecy of their bedrooms they are likely to be as conservative as their most traditional relatives.

These are certainly not the sexually mature people we are talking about. And if any such immature people attempt to follow the mental and physical disciplines we have described in this book, they would be exposing themselves to grave danger. If you do not have the right amount of mental flexibility then your rigid attitudes are likely to be damaged by Tantra.

According to us a sexually mature person is one who believes that any sexual act performed between two consenting adults, provided it does not diminish the right of a third person, is' socially acceptable conduct.

That is the fundamental attitude of a sexually mature person and you and your partner **must** have it if you want to make a success of Tantric sex.

If you and your partner can honestly say that you do have that attitude then only will it be worth your while to go through the questionnaire in this chapter to find out what, exactly, your sexual likes and dislikes are. If you concede that others have the right to do whatever gives them mutual pleasure then you, too, have the right to find out what sexual proclivities, or inclinations, your partner and you have in common. The questionnaire will also help you to find out whether you and your partner are really sexually mature, or merely wishfully think that you are.

How to Use the Questionnaire

Copy out the questions so that you and your partner can answer them separately without prior discussion. Thus the chances of one influencing the other are diminished. Then, when both of you have completed the answers, exchange answer sheets and go through them independently, making a note of the points of divergence. Next, discuss your attitudes towards sex as revealed by the question-aire. Finally, you need not agree but if your differing views are of a fundamental nature than it is best to part rather than risk the danger of a discordant Tantric experience together. We assure you that such a harsh Tantric encounter is much worse than a bad 'trip'.

Questionnaire on Sexual Attitudes

(The questions should be read carefully, thought about and answered with care. There is no time limit for the completion of the questionnaire. Do not discuss the questions with friends or try to ascertain their views on the questions. Do not try to ascertain the views of your partner on the questions till both of you have completed the questionnaire and exchanged answer sheets.)

1. When I see a sexually attractive person I am
   a) aroused b) interested c) cool.
2. I try to find out that person's reaction to me
   a) right away b) in the course of our first meeting
   c) at some future time.
3. If the person is interested I
   a) deliberately engineer our next meeting
   b) hope our next meeting will occur soon
   c) wouldn't go out of my way to find out when we might next meet.
4. When we do meet again I
   a) make a strong play b) make my continued interest apparent but not obvious c) play it cool.
5. To keep a person interested in me sexually I keep the sexual motif in dress, conversation and gestures
   a) strong b) subtle but constant c) underplayed.
6. Friendship between a man and a woman
   a) always has a sexual base b) is usually sexual but may be platonic c) becomes sexual only if one of the two gives it a sexual bias.
7. If a person of the opposite sex made a tactful, but obvious, sexual proposition I would be
   a) flattered b) flustered c) insulted.
8. I can have a satisfying sexual relationship
   a) without love b) only if I pretend that I am in love c) only if I am in love with my sexual partner.
9. Even though my physical capability may decrease with age I believe that my sexual interest will

a) increase b) remain roughly what it is now c) diminish.

10. When I look back at my teen years I
    a) feel I'm far more sexually alive now b) know I have still maintained my sexual awareness c) wish I could be a teenager again, because sexually those were the best years.

11. I had my first sexual experience with a person of the other sex
    a) before I was 11 b) after 11 but before 13 c) between 13 plus and 15 d) between 15 plus and 19 e) after 19.

12. This first experience was
    a) initiated by me b) a mutual thing c) initiated by the other person.

13. That first experience was
    a) stimulating and I wanted more b) stimulating but I was scared off sex for a while c) unsatisfactory.

14. My next sexual experience occurred
    a) within a week of my first b) after a week but within a month c) after a month but within three months d) after three months but within six months e) after six months but within a year f) after a year.

15. Masturbation is
    a) satisfying and often necessary b) satisfying but never necessary c) satisfying but harmful d) not satisfying at all.

16. When I was an adolescent, or a teenager, I have been sexually attracted to persons of my own sex
    a) often b) sometimes c) once d) never.

17. As an adolescent or a teenager I have had a homosexual or lesbian experience
    a) often b) on a few occasions c) once d) never.

18. I feel that homosexuals and lesbians should
    a) be allowed to live their own lives b) be pitied and cured c) be prosecuted for their perversion.

19. Teenage affairs are
    a) a good preparation for life b) a necessary evil c) an unmitigated evil and should be prevented by all means.

20. Now that I am older, when I think back on my first sexual experience
    a) I would like to repeat it to see how it would feel now b) it might be interesting to repeat, but why rake up the past? c) I wouldn't like to go through that again.

21. From the age of 20 till today I have been sexually caressed by
    (Exclude those with whom you have had sexual intercourse)
    a) more than 10 people b) between 5 and 10, inclusive c) between 2 and 4 inclusive d) only 1 person e) none.

22. In this period I have had sexual intercourse with
    a) more than 10 people b) between 5 and 10 inclusive c) between 2 and 4 inclusive d) only 1 person e) none.

23. I first had sexual intercourse when I was
    a) under 15 years of age b) between 15 and 18, inclusive c) between 19 and 24, inclusive d) after 24 e) I have not, as yet, had sexual intercourse.

24. Of the people with whom I had intercourse
    a) more than 10 are now married b) between 5 and 10, inclusive, are now married c) between 2 and 4, inclusive, are now married d) only 1 person is now married.

25. When I had intercourse with them
    a) more than 10 were married b) between 5 and 10, inclusive, were married c) between 2 and 4, inclusive, were married d) only one person was married e) none were married.

26. During my extra-marital affairs I have become pregnant, or, made my partner pregnant
    a) more than 10 times b) between 5 and 10, inclusive c) between 2 and 4, inclusive d) only once e) never.

27. Of these extra-marital pregnancies
    a) more than 10 children were born b) between 5 and 10 children were born c) between 2 and 4 children were born d) only one child was born e) no children were born.

28. I was responsible for the termination of
    (You need not have done it yourself, and restrict your-

self to the pregnancies you caused, or underwent.)
a) more than 10 pregnancies b) between 5 and 10 pregnancies c) between 2 and 4 pregnancies d) only one pregnancy e) no pregnancies.

29. My past experience has led me to treat sex with
    a) enthusiasm b) delight but caution c) great care.

30. I believe sex is best used for
    a) pleasure b) mutual awareness between the sexual partners c) procreation.

31. Birth Control is
    a) essential b) a necessary evil c) totally unacceptable unless a 'natural' method is used.

32. Birth Control is the responsibility of
    a) the man b) both partners c) the woman.

33. During foreplay, Birth Control measures are
    a) an awkward interruption b) totally unacceptable c) fun, because they can be made part of the game.

34. I prefer
    a) the pill b) condoms c) a diaphragm d) the loop or IUCDs e) an operation f) suppositories, foams or jellies g) coitus interruptus h) the 'natural' method i) none of the methods listed above.

35. Thanks to the effectiveness of modern Birth Control methods,
    a) sex has become fun b) there is some hope of controlling the population explosion c) society has become permissive.

36. Regardless of its practical advantages, I believe Birth Control has
    a) opened up new vistas of sex outside the narrow marriage bond b) robbed sex of a certain spontaneity c) become mutual masturbation.

37. Birth Control has done much to dispel sexual fears and taboos. This, in itself, is
    a) a great leap forward b) a mixed blessing c) a dangerous thing.

38. Sexual fears and taboos
    a) are blind superstition b) are distilled wisdom based on practical experience c) are the inner promptings of man, a higher warning which it is dangerous to ignore.

39. Sexual fears and taboos are, basically
    a) the same all over the world b) tailored to suit a specific set of circumstances c) irrelevant in a modern context.

40. By diminishing sexual fears and taboos, Birth Control has made marriage
    a) a more stable and satisfying bond b) face considerable extra-marital competition c) nothing more than licensed prostitution.

41. I believe that a monogamous marriage is
    a) the ideal but not very practical b) a very practical relationship c) absurd and quite unnecessary.

42. Sexual exclusiveness, between marriage partners is
    a) a most workable system b) a social hangover which will change c) entirely impractical in the modern world.

43. Extra-marital relationships, generally
    a) improve a marriage b) put a strain on a marriage c) destroy a marriage.

44. In my marriage I would like to
    a) have no extra-marital affairs b) have extra-marital affairs by mutual consent c) have extra-marital affairs as a matter of right.

45. Number, in order of preference, your choice of the listed alternatives to traditional marriage. Or indicate that none of these appeal to you
    a) Group Marriage: two or more couples sharing partners in a stable marriage relationship b) Partner Swapping: individual couples maintain their separate homes but meet only to exchange partners for temporary sex c) Casual Partners: occasional sexual partners are introduced into an otherwise traditional marriage; the outside partners might be single or married but the essential feature is that the relationship with the outsiders is transient and casual.

46. When my sexual partner touches me in affection, and in public, I
    a) welcome it b) like it but feel awkward c) resent it because there is a time and place for everything.

47. When my sexual partner makes a play for another person in public, even though I know it is only in fun, I
   a) get jealous b) feel a little hurt but accept it c) am amused and proud.

48. When my sexual partner and I are separated temporarily I
   a) am certain that my partner will not have a sexual escapade with another person b) am reasonably confident of my partner's fidelity, but not absolutely certain c) couldn't care less what my partner does d) permit my partner to browse in other pastures.

49. Sexual encounters are
   a) ego building, and should be spoken about openly b) interesting and can be spoken about to close friends c) private affairs and should remain so.

50. An extra-marital relationship in the modern world is
   a) still a private thing b) not as private as it used to be but is still something that should be revealed only to one's friends c) an accepted relationship which need not be concealed.

51. Revealing clothes are worn by
   a) all people who think young b) people who want to run with the herd regardless of their personal attributes c) exhibitionists.

52. If I was with a group of men and women, some of whom I did not know very well, and we saw a topless woman, I would
   a) point her out as just another interesting sight b) feel awkward and say nothing c) try to divert my group's attention away from the exhibitionist woman.

53. A person of my sex, whom I know very slightly, is sitting awkwardly, revealingly, without knowing it, I would
   a) tell a few friends so they might also take in the view b) feel awkward and keep it to myself c) find a mutual friend and pass the word back to the exposed person.

54. What would I do in situation 53 if the person were of the opposite sex?

55. In a resort the men's bathroom is separated from the women's by a thin wall. As I am drying myself in the shower-stall I see two eyes peering at me through an old pipe-duct let into the dividing wall. I would
a) continue to dry myself making sure they got the best view possible b) back against the wall and finish drying myself, hurriedly c) wrap the towel around me, grab a robe, and exit.

56. At a friend's home I walk into a room and find two people making love and know that they've seen me. I
a) say 'Sorry' and close the door behind me b) back out hurriedly, but stay on in the party c) leave the party to avoid facing them when they come out of the room.

57. I go to a picnic without a partner and find everyone pairing off and vanishing behind the dunes. Only one person of the opposite sex is left. I have just met that person. I
a) say 'Care to come for a walk?' hoping that an interesting sexual encounter will develop b) sit down beside the person, in the open, and talk c) stretch out where I am and go to sleep.

59. After the swim they want to take a group photograph with everyone wearing masks and nothing else. I would
a) try and get in the front row b) try and conceal some of my nudity behind somebody else c) say I couldn't join because I was shivering and a cramp would build up right away unless I got dressed immediately.

60. When we get back to the host's home, the lights are doused, we sit on the floor in couples, and blue films are shown. The couples around me are obviously uninhibited. I would
a) grab the opportunity and do likewise b) proceed cautiously because I have only just met my partner c) switch off: I can't take public sex.

61. Erotic movies are
    a) Exciting b) OK if you have the right company
    c) turn me off.
62. Erotic photographs are
    a) best viewed in private with the right companion.
    b) best viewed alone c) sick.
63. Well written erotic literature is
    a) exciting b) interesting c) at best, strictly for mas-
    turbators.
64. The number of erotic books I have read is
    a) over 10 b) between 5 and 10, inclusive c)
    between 2 and 4, inclusive d) one e) none.
65. My sexual fantasies, or erotic day dreams occur
    a) often b) occasionally c) seldom d) never.
66. When I'm sexually attracted by a person I daydream
    about us
    a) holding hands b) kissing c) caressing d) making
    love.
67. When I do fantasize about sex I imagine us dressed
    in exotic clothes
    a) often b) occasionally c) seldom d) never.
68. I imagine us making love before an admiring audi-
    ence
    a) often b) occasionally c) seldom d) never.
69. I imagine myself making love to a number of persons
    of the opposite sex, at the same time
    a) often b) occasionally c) seldom d) never.
70. When I have vivid sexual fantasies I find my body
    responding to my mental pictures
    a) strongly b) mildly c) never.
71. I prefer sexual foreplay to start
    a) long before we reach the place where we are
    going to make love b) only when we're alone but
    before we reach the bedroom c) only after we reach
    the bedroom.
72. Foreplay should be started by
    a) the man b) either of the partners c) the woman.
73. I am most stimulated if foreplay is started
    a) boldly by a word or touch which everyone could
    understand if they heard it or felt it b) in public,
    but secretly by words or gestures which only we

know are erotic c) subtly, like the sound of distant music.

74. In love making, pain plays
    a) an important part b) an occasional role c) no part at all, unless you're a pervert.

75. The use of erotic words and sounds in foreplay
    a) excites me b) does not upset me but I do not use them myself c) turns me off.

76. During foreplay I like
    a) bright lights b) soft illumination c) darkness.

77. Dressing up erotically is
    a) exciting b) OK for my sexual partner but not for me c) absurd.

78. The use of vibrators, brushes, gloves and other equipment during foreplay is
    a) fun b) OK for a change c) perverse.

79. Fellatio and Cunnilingus are
    a) normal and exciting b) OK for a change c) unnatural and sickening.

80. With me foreplay normally lasts
    a) under half an hour b) half an hour to an hour c) an hour to two hours d) over two hours.

81. In intercourse I prefer
    a) the man on top and woman below b) the woman on top and man below c) a variety of positions.

82. If I had my way I would enjoy intercourse most
    a) in a bed b) on the floor c) in the open d) in unusual places.

83. The movements in intercourse should be
    a) quick and passionate b) varied c) slow and controlled.

84. If I see myself in a mirror during intercourse it
    a) excites me b) amuses me c) embarrasses me.

85. During intercourse I normally
    a) fantasize b) think only of my lover c) lose myself in the sensations of lovemaking.

86. I believe that learning to control the muscles used in intercourse is
    a) well worth the effort b) possibly worth while if we could find the time c) pointless in our modern world.

87. I feel that moments of stillness, without movement, at the peak of intercourse
   a) enhance the ecstasy of intercourse b) help to prolong intercourse c) are an unnecessary interruption.
88. Intercourse without orgasm
   a) can be ecstatic in a very special way b) might be necessary but does not add to the pleasure of intercourse c) is incomplete and might be dangerous.
89. In intercourse it is essential to
   a) seek your own satisfaction because your partner's satisfaction will follow as a matter of course b) keep your pleasure in line with your partner's c) seek your partner's ecstasy because then yours will follow.
90. The ecstasy of sex lies in
   a) the body b) the glands c) the mind.

That, then, is the questionnaire.

Here, once again, and in greater detail, is how you should use it.

We have recommended that you and your partner should, at first, examine your answers independently. The reason why we have done this is because then it will be easier for both of you to see co-relationships between the various answers given. The questionnaire has been carefully designed to give an in-depth picture of a person's sexual outlook: similar questions have been rephrased to present a slightly different perspective with each answer. For instance questions 1, 13, 29, 48 73, could be linked to explain your sexual partner's behaviour in the presence of an attractive person of the opposite sex. On the other hand you could also link the answer to question 1 with the answers to questions 46, 65, 83, 86, 87, and 89 to give you a clear picture of your partner's sexual pace. We recommend that you co-relate the answers during a day, or a night, spent away from your partner. Your partner should do the same thing. When you have both got an idea of each others sexual outlook, get together and probe deeper. One method of doing this is for you to take the initiative and say what you feel the answers have revealed, and why you feel that way. Your partner could then do the same for you.

We warn you that this sexual probing can be a harrowing experience, and it is quite likely that your relationship will be put under a severe strain as a result of your sessions. It is for this reason that we recommend that you limit your probing to a maximum of one hour on each side with a 20 minute break in between. And you must make it a point to stop dead on the completion of the hour even though you may be in the middle of a sentence. This discipline helps to establish the therapeutic nature of the probes and whittles down the emotional element. At the end of the 2 hours and 20 minutes we recommend a further 20 minutes break preferably with a change of location or, if that is not possible, a change of lighting and soothing music if both of you like music. Only then should you allow yourselves to become affectionate with each other.

You will find that after every discussion your sex life will become deeper and more meaningful.

There is also the possibility that it will fall apart in which case you can be sure that Tantra would have been very dangerous for both of you and you have thus been saved a much greater emotional disaster.

Apart from giving the partners a great insight into each other's outlook, the questionnaire also forms a jumping-off point for sexual confidences. Who was the first one? Where did it happen? What are the words you like to hear? How do you like to be caressed? Modern sex clinics, starting from Masters and Johnson, realise that much of sexual incompatibility arises from a lack of sexual conversation between couples. The more sexual confidence you exchange the better your sexual relationship is likely to become.

And finally, you cannot be really uninhibited with a person until you hold each others sexual secrets in trust. Few of us can relax sexually unless we are certain that our partner will not 'kiss and tell'. The best insurance against this cowardly practice is a mutual exchange of sexual confidences.

Thus, if properly used, the questionnaire can be a source of sexual renewal and discovery your whole life through. And if either you, or your partner, is reluctant at first, to commit such confidences to writing remember that we have given multiple choice questions: you only have to check off your answers, your writing does not have to appear on the answer sheet at all.

And remember to give the answer **nearest** to your views. The answers provided might not reflect your attitude with a 100% accuracy, but if you check the answer **nearest** the correct one, the marginal error will be compensated in the mass of answers given to the entire questions. The more often you and your partner go over the answers, the more rewarding it will be in terms of mutual understanding. We also recommend that you do the questionnaire at least twice a year to bring out your evolving sexual attitudes.

For the present, however, you will find the questionnaire very useful in planning your wardrobe to suit your individual tastes and fancies in Tantric Sex. We deal with this intriguing task in the next chapter.

Chapter Three

Erotic Dress

You and your partner should have spent at least a week on the last chapter: anything less than that will give you only a superficial knowledge of each other and you cannot depend on a superficial knowledge if you want to tread the Tantric path. But if you have questioned, probed and discussed and feel that you have a good idea of each others sexual attitudes, you can now start amassing your Tantric equipment. Before we speak of the 'equipment', however, we must tell you why we think it is necessary to get such equipment for your Tantric journey.

Men and women are, essentially, polygamous: both like to ring the changes in their sexual partners. Society, however, rules otherwise. Tantra, too, believes that the intensity of the sexual experience among Tantrists is so great that no Tantric practitioner should feel the need to change his partner merely to bring variety into his sexual life. Nevertheless the appearance of variety is often as important as the variety itself: particularly in the initial stages of learning the great secrets. This chapter and the next help provide such a variety to get tyros over the initial period before the endless ecstasy of the Tantric experience suffuses them.

Many reasons have been given for the frequent changes of fashion in the west. This is particularly applicable to women's dress though, of late, men's styles are becoming as fickle. We believe that at the heart of this phenomena lies the stress imposed by monogamy on an essentially polygamous species. Since men and women cannot change their mates every season, their mates can at least give the appearance of having changed. Fashions change, therefore, appearances change, therefore the husband and wife appear to be new people.

Thus, the polygamous instinct is satisfied for another mating season.

Here, again, we must make it clear that this is no part of orthodox Tantra. For that matter we do not claim that this is a traditional Tantric book. If we believed that traditional Tantra could relate to the modern mind, and body, we would not have devoted our time to this book. But, as we have said before, traditional Tantric methods were tailored to a specific age and way of life. We have tried to restate the core of Tantric teaching in 20th century terms and to recast the practices to make them more relevant to our times.

This chapter, then, has been brought about because we believe that without it our readers will find it extremely difficult to make the transition from the cares of day-to-day living to the sexual concentration and tension that is so necessary for Tantric practice.

Specifically the gap between Tantric assumptions.... or rather the assumptions of the Vedic society for which Tantra was tailored....and the western way of thought has occurred because modern occidental mind accepts the validity of certain cultural assumptions, namely:

> that man should be monogamous when his natural instincts tug otherwise;
>
> that the sexual appetites of men and women are polarized: 'nice' women are just not as easily stimulated, sexually, as men, the so-called permissiveness and women's lib notwithstanding;
>
> that certain cultural stereotypes idealise strong sexual images: the fierce 'desert hawk' sheiks, the whip-cord-lean cowboys, the ruthlessly handsome Nazis, the savagely virile African warrior. That is as far as the men go. The women also have their patterned models: the mini-skirted groupie, the braless long-skirted hippie, the bride in virginal white, the Lolita child-mistress in drindl-skirt and pig tails, the savage priestess in metal-mesh bra and beads. The list is endless.

These are essentially modern developments because they could not have existed in a polygamous, non-Madison Avenue society.

No system, therefore that seeks to make ancient teachings relevant to modern times can achieve its purpose unless it acknowledges these developments and finds a way to bridge the cultural gap that these have created. We shall, consequently, start from a fundamental human response, common to all ages of mankind, and proceed from there.

It is an acknowledged fact that nudity, of itself, is non-erotic. Visitors to nudist colonies have often been apprehensive about their anticipated, and overt, sexual response to the visual stimuli of so many nude bodies. But their fears were quite baseless. All nudist colonies insist that their visitors strip before they walk around. And as soon as they strip they realise that they are one with the others and there is no erotic stimulation whatsoever. In fact, they might be surprised to witness a very common phenomenon: if one of the nudist women dresses up to leave the colony on a shopping expedition, her clothed presence is immediately greeted with wolf whistles from the men even though nude girls, with better figures are there for the seeing. What has excited the men is the concealment of the body of the clothed girl. Subtle concealment is erotic, dressing out of context is erotic, nudity in an unusual setting is erotic. And as we, in Tantric sex, are very intimately concerned with sexual stimulus, it is important that we devote much of our time to this subject.

Before we go any further, however, it would help to remember that in Tantra we acknowledge the supreme activity of the Woman; we do not need to adhere to the unisex pattern of the women's libber. We emphasise sexual differences because we know that each has a role to play in the creating and sustaining of the universe: the more the sexual attributes are polarized the greater will be the power generated when the two sexes merge. This, we should like to point out, is diametrically opposite the western-civilization imposed polarization of social attitudes. We know that women have as much erotic sensibility as men; in a way their capacity for erotic stimulation is much greater. Women are multi-orgasmic whereas men are not: it is this sense of male inferiority that has, in all likelihood, prompted men to confine women in an artificial cage of erotic numbness. Tantra releases a woman to give full rein to her erotic potential. The myriad variations of dress figure prominently in the expression of these talents.

Basic to the Tantric woman's erotic wardrobe should be three gauzy scarves: black, red and white. We call them scarves but a north-Indian **do-patta** or **chunni** could fulfil the purpose admirably, as would strips from an old nylon, silk or georgette sari. If they have embroidery, zari, sequins or mother-of-pearl on them, so much the better. The scarf should, preferably, be long enough to go round the neck like a halter....drape the middle of the scarf around the back of the neck with the two ends trailing down the front of the body....cross the scarf across the breasts, around to the back of the body around the hips, joining and coming up between the legs and then circling around the waist like a belt where it can be tied to secure the entire 'garment'. Thus, it covers all the important erotic areas in translucent material, leaves most of the body naked, and is easily removed: the ideal erotic garment.

Take a tip from the attractive Naga women and cover your body in beads: and very little else. Beads are now being produced in the cheapest materials: plastic, wood, seeds and shells apart from the traditional stone. The more colourful the beads are the better but make sure that they are not too heavy to be worn and that they have been strongly strung. It might be worth your while to have them re-strung on strong nylon fishing line or, if you have the time, to do the stringing yourself. The anticipation of the use to which they are going to be put will make your task a light one; it will also maintain your sexual tension throughout the day, a very useful discipline for a Tantrist. Remember, however, that the beads should be long enough to cover you from neck to thigh and that there should be no need to wear anything under them.

If you have never worn high-heeled shoes... if you are a traditional Indian girl, or a very modern one... now is the time to get a pair. Men get an erotic thrill out of seeing a woman in high-heeled shoes because the wearer's calf and thigh muscles are thrown into stimulating relief and the femininity of her carriage is emphasised. Needless to say, all erotic appeal will be lost if the woman trips and falls; it would, thus, be advisable to practice the art of walking in high-heeled shoes in front of a mirror, alone. Wear them during your Tantric rites only when you are confident of staying erect in them, and not a moment before.

Another 'imported' erotic garment is a pair of nylon stockings and if your Tantric mate is not used to seeing you in these their erotic stimulation will be particularly effective. We hesitate to recommend the wearing of nylon stockings, however, because they can be very uncomfortable in our hot climate and you would have to wear a garter belt. But if your Tantric room is air-conditioned, or if you live in a cool climate, then, by all means, buy a pair of nylon stockings making sure that they are not so fine that they can not be seen on your leg. Coloured, patterned or mesh stockings are best. Garter belts are particularly provocative on a nude body and they can be decorated in all sorts of intriguing ways.

The most erotic, public, garment of recent years has been the mini-skirt. If you normally wear saris, or the all-concealing bell-bots and maxis, give your Tantric partner an erotic jolt by turning up in a micro-mini skirt. Please make sure, though, that your figure can take it: fat flabby thighs, an indisciplined stomach and heavy rolls at the waist are femininely concealed in a sari, but they come out into the open in a mini-skirt. But if you have a well-maintained figure... as you should, if you are interested in yourself... a mini-skirt, worn in the privacy of your Tantric Room, will show it up to advantage. If you feel reluctant to go so completely western then use a colourful Naga skirt... which can be made as mini as you like, and is completely Indian... or tie the mini-sari of the Mundas. These uninhibited, and very happy, people tie a waist to mid-thigh length sari, and trail the pallav over their naked breasts. Again a very practical and very Indian dress. You could also wear the mini-sari without the pallav passing over your breasts: cover the upper half of your body with the beads we have suggested earlier.

Proceeding from the feet, knees and thighs we come to the genital area which even the most primitive tribes have, traditionally, covered. As a woman's external genitalia are featureless, this tradition has been a source of considerable argument among anthropologists. If the intention was the covering of the obvious sexual features than men's genitals would have been concealed first: not only are they more obvious, but in excitement, in erection, they are especially attention-attracting and liable to be hurt and damaged. Nevertheless, even our present stone-age societies insist on covering a woman's sexual organs and leaving a man's exposed. Most scientists now agree that primitive man concealed his woman's vulva to protect these generative slits from invasion by malign spirits who might endanger the blood-lines of the entire tribe: even so many women were said to have conceived as a result of impregnation by disembodied spirits. Moreover, a woman is said to be particularly suscepti'le to the evil machinations of eldritch forces during her menstrual flow and, thus, she must conceal her period behind a breech-clout.

Today, the breech-clout has given rise to a large variety of feminine apparel each with its own sexual nuance. Thus if a school-girl mood is to be set, directoire knickers....or 'bloomers' as they used to be called... go well with gym slips. For a more aggressive mood, rubber panties can be teamed up with a leather skirt. The age-old prop of the stripper, the G-string, can easily be made at home. Cut a triangular piece of cloth, large enough to cover the vulva with a little over for hemming. Cut a strip of round elastic to fit snugly around the hips. Sew the two ends of the elastic to the two upper corners of the triangle. Cut another length of round elastic to fit from the third end of the triangle, between the legs, and up. Sew this second bit of elastic to the third, and lower corner of the triangle, taking up the other end of the elastic and sewing it to the centre of the waist-band elastic passing behind your back. You will have to wriggle a bit to make sure the completed G-string fits,

snugly, but once it does you can snip away the loose
ends of the elastic and step into, and out of, your G-
string as you do with an ordinary pair of panties. G-
strings are so easy and economical to make that you
can have as many of them as you like: transparent ones;
others decorated with rhinestones, sequins or embroidery;
one covered in white feathers, another in fur and, if
your partner prefers a blonde, sew a swatch of blond
nylon hair to be worn with a blond wig! (Wigs, however,
are extremely warm and are apt to come off when you
are in the throes of intercourse.)   Particularly convenient are the, so called, crotchless panties. Any knickers,
panties or G-strings can be converted into crotchless
ones by making a slit in the garment to correspond with
the genital opening and then seaming it to prevent fray-
ing.   If your knickers or panties are not skin tight this
opening will be concealed until you part your legs.
Crotchless G-strings can be concealed by covering them
in fur, feathers or nylon hair.   Bikini briefs are abbre-
viated panties that are secured by tapes tied over the
hip bones.

Finally, the last major garment accessories are the
ones that cover the breasts. Here the choice is as large
as those which cover the lower half of the female body
but they are virtually impossible to construct, effectively,
at home.   Our advice on this is that you should buy a
number of commercial brassieres. . . and there are transparent ones, black see-through, front-fastening, deep-
cleavage and a large variety of others. . . .and adapt
them to your needs.   These, too, can be covered with
fur, feathers or rhinestones though, for obvious reasons,
nylon hair is usually taboo as a bra covering.   Here,
again, you could cut away areas directly in front of the
nipples so that these erectile tissues thrust out through
the uplifting bras.

From the advertisements appearing in the papers there
would appear to be no lack of variety in the bras and
panties available to Indian women so there should be
no difficulty in fabricating erotic garments out of them.
We would, however, recommend an important erotic
garment which is not available in the market in our

country. We refer to the Stripper's Pastie: it goes particularly well with the G-String.

Pasties are easily constructed by cutting a circle out
of heavy buckram. The circle should cover your nipples and a bit more, a diameter of $4\frac{1}{2}$ cm or 2 inches
usually sufficing. Make a cut from the circumference
to the centre of the circle and lap over the ends of the
slit to form a cone, sticking or sewing them together.
And that's it. Cover the pasties with sequins, rhinestones,
fur or whatever else you wish, and trim off the tip if
you want to expose the nipples. Then, when you want
to fit them into place, use adhesive tape. . .rolled into a
thin tube with the sticky side out and stuck around the
inner side of the cone, then pressed to your breasts. . .
or spirit gum. The effect that such pasties have on men
is testified to by the generations of successful ecdysiasts!

In addition to the major garment accessories there
are some minor ones.

If you have a reasonable waist, or well developed
breasts, try using a broad leather belt to emphasise the
aggressively manly look: a shock erotic contrast with
the nude female body wearing it! The belt, to be effective, should not be less than 7 cm or 3 inches in width
and, if you have the choice, studded with metal and with
circular holes cut out every $2\frac{1}{2}$ cm or a little more than
an inch apart. This could be worn alone or with a short
skirt, and nothing else. If, however, you feel that your
Tantric partner is not ready for such a dramatic effect,
wear a more feminine metal belt: particularly effective
is the heavy, gold, oddianam belt worn by the traditional
Tamilian bride.

Because the Indian girl does not normally wear hats
these accessories are likely to have great erotic appeal if
worn with a flair. Many of the younger actresses are
often shown in hats of various shapes and sizes, standing or lounging provocatively. The large, floppy-brim-
med hats. . . a national women's magazine recently gave
details of how to make one. . . .are effective when worn
with nothing else. Other moods can be captured with
the solar topi (Hunter-wali), service officers' caps (the
startched military look) and astrakhans (South Indian

politicians and female spies). All should be worn with dark glasses and, if possible, with an open sun-shade.

Finally, no accessory, can be more erotic than jewellery worn on a naked body. Rings, earrings, necklaces, bangles take on a new meaning when displayed against the warm contours of a nude woman and even the most inexpensive trinkets flash with stimulation when worn in this setting. Try it: the effect is startling.

And now for some other interesting, though non-essential, erotic garments.

The most popular erotic garment continues to be the nightie, and few can go wrong with a black, glass-nylon version with a very full skirt trailing down to the ground. An increasing number of Indian women are taking to this very practical night garment and they are readily available in all the larger towns. But even if you have never worn one we recommend that you start right away. The occasional glimpses of your naked body underneath the almost see-through nylon can raise a man's erotic pressure as few other garments can. If you wear gold or red bras or panties under it the effect can be even more stimulating.

The films have made much of the harem girl and most men have been conditioned to be erotically stimulated by the harem look. This is very easy to achieve in our country. Make yourself a North-Indian salwar in some gauzy material and wear it with a short, embroidered jacket or waistcoat fashionable with the young men in Lucknow, and a veil across the lower half of your face.

Gypsies have also, rightly or wrongly, passed into erotic legend for their proverbial passionate nature. The fiery gypsy girl is a favourite film stereotype and the impact of this imagery in men's minds can be used with advantage. Some people say that the gypsies came from Rajasthan and the Rajasthani's dress is certainly very bright and gypsy-like. Wear a Rajasthani gathered skirt, or lehenga, with the typical mirror-work blouse. For a more daring effect, make the blouse in see-through material and have the mirrors stitched on so as to conceal the nipples.

The topless look can be startlingly achieved by wearing a blouse ... or choli ... and skirt. For the skirt we recommend the Assamese mekhla which is colourful, easy to tie and hugs the figure. The impact of this erotic garment is given, however, by cutting holes in the blouse so that the breasts can protrude from an otherwise very- modest garment.

If you have a good figure we suggest that you try wearing a sari the Coorgi-way... draped sheath-like across the front of the body and then over one shoulder. It should, however, be worn without bras or blouse so that the movements of the naked breasts under the single fold of the sheer material are clearly visible.

An imaginative Tantrist could also consider enhancing her wardrobe with:

* a hessian poncho; a length of soft, bleached, 'gunny-bag' cloth folded over so that it drapes from your shoulders to cover your front and back, and with a hole for your head to project from; the sides open; a broad embroidered band of flowers at the bottom ... cheap, easy to make and startlingly effective.

* an ordinary sari petticoat worn tied immediately below the naked breasts; if necessary, increase the length of the drawstring so that you can tie it around your neck and thereby give some- support to the breasts.

Incidentally, all these garments have been 'wear-tested' by a very advanced Tantric friend who, in spite of the fact that she has little need for such props now, still uses them to stimulate her partner when the mood takes them, though it is never as planned an assault on the senses as it used to be.

We have dealt, so far, with women's erotic dress and have said nothing about the male Tantric partner. This is to be expected because 20th century man is still a prosaic dresser though, of late, there appears to be a change for the better. In spite of this change, however, the basic shirt-trouser-jacket combination remains, with only minor variations. The male Tantrist will, therefore, have to cast further afield in his search for erotic apparel.

There are very few women who are not stirred by the primitive look and if you have a good physique, broad wristbands on both forearms, a bracelet around one of your biceps, a single ear-ring, broad belt and a loin-cloth, should convey the right message.

Alternatively, the Englishmen of a former era had the right idea with tight hose and cod-pieces to emphasise the thrust of the genitals. Nowadays, with stretch materials clinging like a second skin, there should be no need for cod-pieces and, we have found that enterprising garment manufacturers have already introduced such lines in the west.

If the woman Tantrist favours the romantic look, stretch hose can be worn with raglan sleeved shirts, open to the waist. Artists of the Victorian and Edwardian era often depicted their poets and musicians in this apparel and women's magazines still favour the look in their illustrations.

Bikini briefs are also being fashioned for men and they seem to be particularly popular when worn with fish-net vests.

But by far the most stimulating erotic garment for men, if the Swedish magazines are to be believed, are fish-net bikinis in bright colours. Most of the male performers in the porno illustrations dress in these functional garments, when they dress at all. And since erotic stimulation is their business we conclude that this garment gives the greatest erotic impact.

Finally, if nothing else is available, a bright, well-fitting pair of swimming briefs, with a front opening, is a very practical, and stimulating, garment for most erotic situations.

These, then, are some of the variations of erotic dress that have been used by practicing Tantrists of our age. It might well be that you and your Tantric partner have no need of these props because, and we would like to make this quite clear, erotic dress is little more than a prop. If our ideas of sex and eroticism were not conditioned by the contradictory pressures of society we would be satisfied with the Tantric symbolism of the Shakti's Red Robe evoking ideas of passion, marriage and re-birth. But our appreciation of such subtle nuances has been dulled under the battering of today's mass media. We want things presented to us in as gross a form as possible otherwise they make no impact on our jaded minds.

We cannot force the mind, suddenly, to attune itself to the subtle world around it. But we can, by gradual enticement and re-education, draw it back to an appreciation of the finer gradations of experience. We do this by feeding it with the gross stimulus to which it has become accustomed: unsubtle erotic dress. We then make it sensitive to the atmosphere that surrounds that dress leading it away from a preoccupation with mere physical stimulus to the mental climate that exists behind that stimulus and thus to the subtly exquisite ecstasies of Tantric Sex.

It is in this quest for increasing subtlety that we take you to the next phase of your Tantric journey.

would be seduced with the Tantric symbolism of the
Shakti's Red Robe, evoking ideas of passion, marriage
and re-birth. But the symbolism of such subtle nuances has been dulled under the battering of today's mass
media. We are so accustomed to us as gross a
form as possible that now they make no impact on
our jaded minds.

We recall here the ancient custom of many societies

Chapter Four

The Tantric Room

You are about to embark on a journey in search of
your Self. We shall never tire of emphasising this point
because in it lies the purpose, the joy and the danger of
Tantra. The purpose of Tantra is to find Who you are.
The joy of Tantra lies in the nature of the quest and
the bliss of the eventual discovery. The danger of Tantra is that your 'psyche' . . . we use this inadequate word
for want of anything better. . .is a delicate and sensitive
thing. From the time you are born, and face the hostile
world, you build up layers of defensive shields, like
tough horny shells, around your easily-hurt image of
yourself. Before you can make any progress in Tantra
you have to scale off these protective carapaces and
allow the soft, palpatating 'you' to be touched, and to
touch. It is only at this contact-level that you can lose
your society-built identity and begin to merge with the
larger identity that is your potential. But the 'peeling'
process is something which leaves you very vulnerable
and if you should get a shock at this time it will be very
difficult to recover from it. This is roughly what happens
when one partner in a passionate love affair is unfaithful
to the other. The lovers have bared themselves to each
other. The unfaithful lover, however, has had time to
re-establish the protective layers secretly. The other
has not been warned to do so. When the abrupt break
comes, the jilted lover finds himself, or herself, exposed
to a harsh world without the defensive barriers. Some
go mad, others commit suicide, most become cynical:
cynicism is the result of building additional, de-sensiti-
zing, layers because of such a hurtful experience. No
cynic can be a Tantrist and no Tantrist can be a cynic.
It is, therefore, of primary importance that the partners
in a Tantric quest are insulated from the intrusion of the
outside world.

Tantra does this by placing the Tantrists in a mandala or protective diagram that concentrates and focuses the psychic and mental forces.

You should do it by ensuring that your Tantric Room ....the laboratory in which you will conduct the search into your Selves... is well equipped and locked, bolted and barred from outside intrusion.

But first you must have a Tantric Room.

We realise that many of our readers will not be able to set aside a separate room for Tantra and, quite frankly, we do not see the need to do so. The bedroom could serve both purposes adequately but, if you are building your own house, the bedroom could be designed especially for Tantra.

To start with, the room should be located at one end of the house, preferably with a view. One of the best Tantric apartments we have seen juts out on a spur, thrusting from the main body of the hill-top house in a broad-based L, enclosing a tiny garden at the spur's tip. The garden-facing walls of the apartment are floor-to-ceiling sliding glass doors giving a breathtaking view of the garden and the hills beyond. The vertical arm of the L holds the bath-and-dressing rooms; the base of the L is the Tantric Room.

The seclusion, the view, the access to the outdoors and the fact that the room cannot be overlooked are four important considerations when planning the ideal Tantric Room and we shall speak of each factor separately.

It is necessary to be secluded from the rest of the house because you should not be disturbed by the daily activities of the household. Any noise... the servants working, the children playing, the phone ringing... might break your Tantric concentration with disappointing results. If, therefore, you cannot seclude yourself and your partner in a room at the end of the house then you will have to time your Tantric exercises for the quiet hours; the afternoon or the night. This is the solution that most Tantric couples are forced to take, it is not the ideal solution but it is acceptable.

A view, a sense of open-ness, helps considerably in achieving a mind-expanding empathy with all nature. This, possibly, accounts for the fact that honeymooners prefer beach resorts and hill-stations for their getting-to-know-each-other days. They seem to realise, instinctively, that they are trying to build up a new and expanded personality, one that will embrace the merged personalities of the bride and the groom: horizon-spanning vistas help in achieving this greater consciousness. It is sad that the empathic drive of the honeymoon is, so easily, stifled under the cares of daily living. Tantric lovers, however, are always on their honeymoon.

Making love under the open sky seems to bring back a sexual understanding that urban-mankind has lost. It not only lends variety to your sex life, and makes for a fresh burst of spontaneousness, it is also a totally new experience. Quite apart from our hill-top friends, at least two of our town-dwelling acquaintances have tiny gardens attached to their bedrooms: one has converted a balcony into a green dell, another has partitioned off a back verandah. Neither of them are Tantrists but they are imaginative people and we feel certain that these little atriums play a very active part in their love life.

Which brings us to the fourth point: overlooking. If you intend to make, and use, a Love Garden, please ensure that it is not overlooked by any of your neighbours. Our Tantric friends on the hill-top house have no hills looming over them and so, short of a helicopter, they are immune from Peeping Toms. The problem is a little more difficult to solve in a town, but awnings and canopies are usually the answer. Please check that your awnings, walls and partitions are peer-proof by looking around while you lower yourself from your normal standing height all the way down to floor level. We recall the embarrassment caused to guests in a new hotel in Delhi. The shower was fixed in front of the neck-to-knee level bathroom window. Between the window and the shower was an opaque shower curtain which every guest pulled across before bathing. And those

guests who happened to be in the swimming-pool at
night got a multi-storey high view of unsuspecting bath-
ers: the shower curtains came down only as far as the
waist but no bather had noticed it!

We also recommend that you carry out the same peer-
proof checks with your Tantric Room windows and
skylights. Remember that the room will have to be well
ventilated because the oxygen consumption of the human
body is high during prolonged intercourse.

Next, the doors. Bolt your Tantric Room doors, and
bar them and padlock them if necessary. But whatever
you do make sure that no one can barge in when you
and your partner are there together. If you have children,
teach them from an early age, that you are not to be
disturbed when your door is locked. Tell them any
story you like... the favourite, and not untrue, one is
that you are both doing exercises, or yoga, or praying
or contemplating. We also recommend that you should
have a curtain on the Tantric Room side of the door
to protect you and your partner from key-hole peepers.

We also believe that it would be best if the room and
the door were sound-proofed. You must be totally uninhibited in your lovemaking and you cannot be totally
uninhibited unless you are able to call, cry out or shout
in the throes of sexual ecstasy. Most old houses, and
those built in suburban areas, have walls that are thick
enough to deaden all but the loudest cries, but this is
not so in our modern flats. Sound proofing is a little
expensive but we put it higher in our Tantric Room prio-
rity list than a comfortable bed: you can make uninhibited love on a mattress, or even on a rug on the floor,
but you cannot make uninhibited love in a sound-leak-
ing room. And if you cannot make uninhibited love
then Tantra is not for you.

That, then, takes care of the essentials. We now get
down to the second stage: the equipment that is not
essential for your Tantric Room, but helpful.

A bed is not essential for lovemaking but it is helpful.
We recommend the standard-shape bed, longer than it
is broad and not one of the fancier circular, octagonal or
triangular jobs. It should, of course, be a double bed

with a single mattress covering the entire sleeping area. Twin mattresses are apt to part in the middle under the activity of Tantric Sex. Unless the Tantric partners are unusually built, a mattress area of 200 cm (6½ feet) by 140 cm (4½ feet) should be adequate. As for the mattress, though we have heard much about the pneumatic bliss of a water-bed, we recommend a board bed with close fitting wooden planks over which you should have a foam-rubber mattress. This combination is just right: soft enough for comfort and firm enough to give support in even the most complicated asanas.

If you intend to make a bed... and not merely buy a ready-made bed... ensure that the height is just right. This can be measured in a very practical way. If the female partner crouches on all fours on the bed... resting on her elbows, forearms and knees... in what is referred to by Van de Veld as the Flexed or Kneeling Attitude, sexual intercourse is effected from behind. This is also known as the Ram Position or **El kebachi** in Nefzawi's. The Perfumed Garden. You and your partner should get into this position, with the woman kneeling on the bed: the bed and mattress should be high enough to let you have intercourse in this attitude without requiring the man to crouch or stand on tip toes, or for the woman to be raised by pillows. For the average couple a floor-to-top-surface-of-mattress height of 61 cm (24 inches) should be convenient, give or take 5 cm (2 inches).

We do not believe in an elaborate headboard because it adds to clutter and is apt to be distracting.

Next, for your Tantric Room, you should have a good floor rug if you do not have wall to wall carpeting. The rug should be at least 185 cm (6 feet) by 92 cm (3 feet), have a firm, but not fluffy, pile, a foam underlay, and, if possible, anti-slip treads. It is important that the rug does not slip out from under your feet or body and if you cannot get the treads, think of some way to fasten the carpet in position, if not permanently at least during your Tantric sessions.

Along with the carpet you should also get at least six, firm, cotton filled cushions of varying sizes but not larger than 46 cm square (18 inches by 18 inches) and about 20 cm (8 inches) thick at their deepest. We do not recommend foam rubber cushions because the cushions might have to be bent and folded to support the body in various sexual asanas and foam rubber does not lend itself to this use. For the same reason do not have the cushions too tightly packed with cotton. You should also have a columnar bolster, 60 cm (24 inches) long and 25 cm (10 inches) in diameter. This should be firmly stuffed with cotton as it will be used as a back support, if you should need it; a foam rubber bolster would do as well.

Another helpful bit of equipment is a low, broad-based, armless chair. The seat of the chair should not be more than 26 cm (10 inches) off the ground, with a really broad resting surface and a firm, high, back. We recommend that the chair should be made out of wood with the emphasis on strength rather than on beauty. Both the seat and the back should be designed to take foam rubber cushions and the cushions should be cloth covered: rexine and the so-called leather cloth is apt to become quite slippery against a nude body and they can get cold in winter and hot in summer. The seat of the chair should be broad enough to support the back of a person lying on it with his, or her, legs thrust up against the back of the chair. Similarly, the back of the chair should be high enough to support the head of the taller of the two partners, sitting in the chair. You should also have two other chairs: standard, armless, dining-room chairs, as stable as possible.

And, finally, there is the mirror. This marks the border-line between the helpful equipment and the luxury trimmings. One mirror is helpful and, if you can have only one, a long narrow mirror can serve your purpose excellently: 30 cm (1 foot) by 122 cm (4 feet) is a good size. If it is possible, mount it vertically on a wall so that you can look into it from somewhere on the bed, preferably beyond the foot of the bed.

But, if you have the inclination and the space, fill the room with mirrors: mirrors lining the walls at the two ends of the bed... these are the best... the two side walls and, for the really sybaritic touch, on the ceiling.

Soft lights and mirrors produce the most erotic images and the sight of yourselves making love, multiplied infinitely, is an experience that must be seen to be believed. A word of warning, though: there are times when you and your partner want to be alone and you cannot be alone in a Tantric Room full of mirrors. You can solve this by draping curtains in front of the mirrors and this has the advantage of giving the room a comfortable, closed, feeling when you want the feeling most. Our friends in the spur house solved it in their own, original way. When you enter their bedroom you get an impression of soft pink and grey. The huge windows are curtained in dusty rose-pink, and the rest of the walls, and the entire ceiling, is covered in quilted, dove-grey, diamond-shaped, panels. It is a soothing, warmly feminine room. And if you want to change it into Pompadour's boudoir you press the appropriate buttons and the panels swing around to reveal their mirrored rears and conceal their quilted fronts. It never ceases to make an impact on anyone who sees it.

The use of effective lighting is something else we have learnt from our friends. At the centre of every quilted panel, and stitched into the draped curtains, are hundreds of little bulbs which can be lit in varying patterns or set to blink in sequence. The most unusual effect is when the curtains are drawn over the windows, the lights on them lit, and the mirrors on the other two walls exposed. Alternatively, the lights on the walls can be switched off and the ceiling lights set to glow like stars. The combinations are virtually infinite and, to add to the choice, they also have indirect lighting concealed in the pelmets and tiny, bright, swivled spot lights mounted at eight places in the room. The entire lighting can be controlled by a battery of variable-intensity switches.

We have described this elaborate illumination in some detail because we want you to appreciate the infinite possibilities of lighting: it can virtually complement, or even set, any mood. We realise, of course, that most of our readers will not be able to afford anything nearly so complex, but with the selection of lighting fixtures available nowadays it should not be too difficult to give fairly free rein to your imagination when planning the illumination of your Tantric Room.

Another sexual mood-setter is music. Shakespeare merely expressed common knowledge when he said that music is the food of love; it is, in fact, the food of all emotions. The right music, in the right quantity, is bound to bring on the right mood. The secret has been used with telling effect in the ragas but, regrettably, most westernized Indians do not have the right cultural background to respond to the subtle impact of the ragas. This does not mean, of course, that the westernized person cannot use the stimulus of music: it only means that we shall have to search further afield to find the right harmonies. You should, if you want to make use of this stimulus, have a music system fitted in your bedroom and the rig should be able to handle both records and tapes. It is entirely up to you to choose between stereo, quadro and wrap-around sound, but remember that you will be playing most of the music as softly as possible: the sensitivity of the set is important, not its volume.

The choice of music is largely a personal matter because Indian classical music is divided into a number of distinct disciplines unlike the single mainstream of western classical music today. Thus, if you and your partner are western classical music fans, we would recommend the second act of Wagner's **Tristan and Isolde,** Beethoven's **Kreutzer Sonata,** Berlioz' **Symphonie Fantastique** and the garden scene from Gounod's **Faust.** If folk melodies are your forte then try the raw sexuality of African drums and tribal chants, the throaty ululation of Egyptian music, and the compulsive guitar melodies of Spain. For timeless erotic enchantment, however, there is nothing in the world to compare with the sitar, the sarod, the shehnai and the Indian flute... played solo, and not in their modern orchestrated form. But, as we have said, response to music is a very personal matter and if the much maligned 'filmi' music has the desired effect on you and your partner then you should have no hesitation in using it in your Tantric Room.

These are merely suggestions and the final choice of music will depend entirely on your subjective response.

What we do suggest, however, is that regardless of your choice of music, it must be played softly. It is customary, nowadays, to turn the volume on as high as possible. Nothing can be further from the Tantric approach. Tantra tries to heighten your sensitivity, your awareness of the myriad subtle gradations of stimuli available to your senses. Over stimulation deadens this sensitivity and wipes out weeks of effort. The only over-stimulation that you and your partner must allow yourselves is sexual ecstasy which is in itself, the cumulative effect of a number of subtle stimuli: the rough velvet feel of an erect nipple; the subtle aroma of sexual excitement; the taste of your lover's skin; the sound of a caught breath at the peak of orgasm; the sight of a pupil dilating as ecstasy roars through the body. All these responses will be hidden from you unless you teach your senses to become sensitive again. Do not, we advise you, drown your senses in blaring sound: that is not music. Keep the music soft, understated, and very much in the background. The music should accompany your lovemaking, it should not batter it.

You could also try using a tape recorder to pick up the whispered words and the other sounds of pleasure. A tape recorder is a most unobtrusive spectator and you and your partner will soon forget that it is on, but once the recording has been made it will become a valuable addition to your erotic library.

Yes, you must have an erotic library in your Tantric Room and of all the places in the world such a library should be easiest to build up in our country. To start with, the timeless erotic classics **Kama Sutra**, **Kok Shashtra** and **Ananga Ranga** provide an unequalled and classical range. Erotic art is part of the heritage of India and no Indian should be ashamed to own, and display, examples of it when foreigners travel halfway round the world to get a glimpse of these great treasures. Picasso's erotic sketches and, Guilio Romano's Posizioni series are insignificant when compared with Konarak, Khajuraho and Bhubaneshwar. As for the rest, the open shelves of most book shops display a wide variety of exotic literature to suit every taste. Here we must dispute the com-

monly held belief that women, as a rule, are not erotically stirred by books and illustrations. That might have
been true for an older generation but it did not arise out
of any inherent quality in women, it was merely because
women had been brought up to believe that 'nice' girls
do not respond to such erotic stimuli. Modern education,
and today's way of life, have done much to break down
these artificial barriers and the Tantric male can now
expect his partner to be as erotically stirred as he is,
when they both look at a well-chosen erotic library.

The best illustrations of all, of course, are photographs
of yourselves making love. These used to be difficult to
obtain because partners were reluctant to trust such ex-
posures to the processing of commercial studios. Nowadays, however, with the Polaroid camera and its self-
printing films, these inhibitions need no longer hold them
back: use a self-timer, a cable shutter release, or snap
yourselves in a mirror. But there is something even better than a Polaroid camera for erotic pictures: the Video-
Tape. If you can get hold of one of these devices there
will be no limit to what you can do for your erotic library.

And if your erotic library has a selection of the glossy
Scandanavian erotic magazines you will have noticed
how they use science's latest gift to erotics: the hand
vibrator. We advise you to get the tube-shaped (it looks
very much like an erect penis) battery-powered model,
available freely in electronically-advanced and liberal
minded countries. The more specialized ones come with
a variety of attachments which give a wide range of
stimuli, but even the simplest ones can do wonders if
correctly applied to the erotically-sensitive parts of the
body. Remember again, however, that your touch must
be delicate: you and your partner must teach yourselves
to appreciate the delicate nuances, the finer shades, of
feeling, rather than to bring yourselves to a sexual climax
with the vibrator.

Which brings us to the last, and most unlikely, attachment to your Tantric Room: the Bathroom.

Later on in this book we shall talk about Sex Hygiene
so we will not elaborate on that theme now, but you
must realise that the physical contact of Tantric Sex is

so intimate that both partners must ensure that their bodies are impeccably clean. There must be no occasion when one partner is even mildly put off by the slightest lack of hygiene in the other. The ancient Indians were aware of this and thus Tantric sculptures and paintings frequently dwell on women bathing or at their toilet. It would appear that as sexual expression becomes more frustrated, the human body becomes less hygienic. Today, however, hygiene and particularly sexual hygiene, has come into its own again.

To start with, if you can afford it opt for a sunken bath and one as large as the room can take. Oriental erotic treatises describe many specialised sexual positions that can be achieved in a sunken bath and, for a variation of the sexual diet, lovemaking in a bath has much to recommend it. We would advise, however, that you ensure that part of the bottom of your sunken bath is floored with anti-slip tiles, and that you install a rubber-covered hand-rail all around. This can be recessed into the sides of the sunken bath for safety: we can think of many occasions when you and your Tantric partner would want to get a firm grip on the rail whilst you were otherwise engaged. And if you do decide to make a sunken bath try and have a whirlpool machine fitted into it: bathing becomes a totally new experience with the churning water hitting against your naked body.

Mirrors : again plenty of them on the walls and, if possible, on the ceiling. Make sure that they are good mirrors because otherwise they might get discoloured, soon, with the steam and water of the bath.

And as there is little point in having mirrors unless you have illumination, use your imagination when lighting up the bathroom.

A soft, absorbent, rug is another useful fitting for your bathroom and we do not mean a bath-mat. This rug should be big enough for you and your partner to roll on and love on when you come out of your bath and it should be anchored firmly to the floor.

Take a suggestion from the public baths of the Indus Valley civilization and install a hot-air fan in the bathroom: it is a sensuous way for your partner and you to dry yourselves and it brings the blood to the skin making it responsive to erotic touches and caresses.

And do not forget the bidet: an excellent bit of sex hygiene equipment now becoming increasingly popular all over the world. We feel so strongly about this sensible invention that we almost put it into the essential equipment category but then we remembered that we were writing largely for asian readers, and since asians make a practice of washing themselves more thoroughly than others do, we decided to keep the bidet among the luxuries.

All of which begs the question: why must Tantra, essentially a mental and psychic discipline, rely so heavily on luxuries? The answer is that Tantra does not rely on luxuries, it uses them. Great scientists have made great discoveries in the humblest of laboratories. This fact, however, does not diminish the achievement of those who have made equally great discoveries in well equipped laboratories. Tantra is a search for the wellsprings of your Self. It is a voyage of self-discovery and so it is a very private, a very personal, journey and one that will call for all the resources at your command. When you use these resources, a bedroom is not just a bedroom: it is an essential part of your laboratory of joy. And as the best results generally come from the best equipped laboratories, you owe it to yourself and to your partner to make your Tantric Room as well equipped as you can.

But the principle instrument in your laboratory is always, and every time, your body and mind, and the body and mind of your partner. The next few chapters will be devoted to the tuning of these delicate instruments of Tantric Sex.

Chapter Five

Scent, Taste and Sex Hygiene

Sexual intimacy is the method of Tantra, and it is an intimacy of such intensity that the partners loose themselves in each other. But before they reach this ego-dissolving ecstasy their psychic barriers have to be broken down by protracted physical contact. And it 'is in this close physical contact that a grave danger lies: unless the partners are scrupulously, physically, clean their senses of smell and taste will revolt and the Tantric sexual bond will be broken. It is to avoid this disaster that we have given a whole chapter to this important subject.

The sense of smell and the sense of taste are, in many ways, akin. Flavour, for instance, is a merging of both. Most people, if they pinch their nostrils together and close their eyes, will not be able to tell the difference between a slice of potato and a similarly shaped slice of apple. The tastes of the vegetable and the fruit will be exactly the same. The smell and the taste of the apple and potato have to go together to produce the distinguising quality called flavour. It is for this reason too that people with colds suffer from a loss of appetite: their food has no flavour and so they do not want to eat it.

The tongue can really distingush only four tastès: sweet, sour, bitter and salt. All foods have one or more of these tastes but it is the smell of the food mixed with the taste that gives us the wide, and subtle, range that has enthralled gourmets throughout history.

Thus, the sense of smell plays a very important part in our lives and, whether we know it or not, our reactions to people are conditioned by a subliminal assessment of their personal odours. This is particularly valid in the field in which we are interested: sexual attraction and repulsion.

Personal odour is created mainly by the sweat glands. These tiny glands cover the entire skin though there is a higher concentration of them in some parts of the body than in others. They lie in the scond layer of skin, the dermis, and one of their jobs is to keep us cool by drawing water from the blood-stream and allowing it to evaporate on the surface of the skin. But, along with the water, the sweat glands also pick up tiny particles of other substances in the blood and, because there are so many glands, the smell of these other substances becomes the main ingredient of our distinctive scent. It is a commonly held belief among animal trainers that beasts who associate with man are able to sense his moods: his fear, happiness, confidence. This, they say, is nothing more than the beast's awareness of our inner state as revealed by the tiny secretions of our skin; in other words, our personal odour.

While most of our personal odour originates in our skin, much of it is evaporated and neutralised by the air and sunlight. It is a fact that the concentration of your personal odour increases with the amount of clothing you wear. People in cold countries, muffled up in heavy garments, have a more distinctive personal odour than people in warmer lands, other things being equal. This is because fibres. . . . synthetics and the natural fibres such as cotton, linen, silk, fur and hair. . . . have the effect of retaining and concentrating such odours. This is true even of our natural, body, fibres: hair. Hair traps sweat and, while the more volatile parts of sweat evaporate, the heavier ingredients are held by the hair and their scent is, thus, intensified. This is particularly so when hair grows between folds of skin, which further retard evaporation, such as the hair under the armpits or covering the genital area.

The second important source of personal odour is the mouth. As we all know, the mouth and the throat have to be constantly lubricated to be in a state of health. The body achieves this by secretions of various glands, such as the salivary glands, and a constant renewal of certain specialised cells that die and are replaced by new cells. This entire defensive and lubricatory process gives rise to a distinctive aroma and a person's state of health can often be fairly accurately discerned by the scent of the breath.

Finally, although all personal odours have a sexual association, the only really sexual odours originate in the sexual glands. In men the distinctive, faintly mushroom-like, scent of semen is imparted by the prostatic fluid. This fluid, produced by the prostate gland, is necessary to make the sperm active. Till the sperm come into contact with the fluid of the prostate they are quiescent and quite unfit for the long journey up the woman's uterus. This journey is many thousands of times longer than the tiny sperm and during the course of the journey they have to cross over the 'mountainous' folds and ridges of the mucus of the uterus, the outward stroking 'hairs' of the oviduct, and the hostile chemical composition of this dark region. Thus, the motility imparted by the prostatic fluid is essential to the very survival of mankind. It is, therefore, not difficult to understand why the scent of this precious liquid plays such an important part in the attraction between the sexes.

While the scent of semen gives a strong erotic stimulus, the strongest sexual scent is found in the genital organs of women. Like many other things we have this in common with most mammals, and while we do not display our sexual intentions as frankly and uninhibitedly as dogs, we do exhibit the same basic reactions in our own 'civilized' way.

Most of a woman's sexual organs are internal and, thus, the source of her sexual scent is also hidden. Scientists are not entirely sure of the exact origin of the sexual odour of women and they confine themselves to saying that it is a combination of many secretions that help lubricate the genital tract. This can be better understood if we know a little about a woman's genital organs and what happens to them when she is sexually excited.

A woman's sexual organs consist of a protective pad of tissue known as the **mons veneris** which, in the case of a mature woman, is covered in pubic hair. In the centre of the mons veneris is the slit of the vulva which is the external entrance to the genital organs. This slit is closed by two pairs of vertical lips, the **labia manora** and the **labia minora,** one pair below the other. At the upper junction of the labia minora, the little lips, is the clitoris, like a miniature penis. After the little lips there is a very specialised structure known as Bartholins Glands. Beyond these glands, and built into the walls of the entrance of the vagina, are the strong, circular muscles known as the **constrictor cunni.** After them is the vagina, where the sperm is normally ejected during sexual intercourse. The vaginal walls are deeply folded, elastic, muscular and lubricated with mucus. And at the end of the vaginal chamber, projecting into it like a stopper into a bottle, is the mouth of the uterus: this mouth is called the cervix. Beyond the cervix is the triangular chamber of the uterus on the walls of which the fertilized egg will lodge. Before its fertilization, the female egg, or ova, leaves an ovary on maturity, descends through the oviduct where it should meet a sperm and be fertilized, and then falls into the uterus.

As neither the ovary nor the oviduct produce any discernible secretions which effect the personal odour of a woman, we shall not consider them any further.

Normally, the uterus produces a mucus secretion which plugs the mouth of the uterus. In moments of sexual excitement, the contractions of the uterus eject this plug into the vagina. Here, the mucus plug mixes with the mucus of the vagina and flows out through the vaginal opening. We would like to make it clear that a healthy vagina is always lubricated by its mucus in the same way that a healthy throat is, also, always damp. Thus, this mucus does flow out, at all times, through the vaginal opening and this accounts for the primary feminine odour. In sexual excitement, however, the mucus of the uterus and the mucus of the vagina increase their flow appreciably because their tissues have become engorged with blood: the equivalent of the male erection. In addition to these two fluids, prolonged sexual excitement also causes the Bartholins Glands to add their distinctive odour. The purpose of these glands has not been completely established but many scientists believe that their chief function is to provide a stimulating sexual odour.

Finally, if the ova is not fertilized, the entire lining of the uterus dissolves and flows out along with the unfertilized egg in the process known as menstruation: commonly known as a woman's 'periods'. The menstrual flow, too, has its own odour which many men find erotically stimulating.

There are thus four separate sources of the scent of a woman's sexual organs: the faint, normal, aroma of the constantly lubricating vaginal mucus; the scent of the first stages of sexual excitement, consisting of a merging of the mucus of the uterus and the vagina; the erotic smell of heightened sexual stimulus which also includes the distinctive secretions of Bartholins Glands; and the odour of the menstrual flow.

These, then, are the many origins of personal odour: sweat, breath and genital scent. None of these odours, in their original state, are erotically repugnant to the opposite sex, including the aroma of the menstrual flow. However, if the residue of these secretions are allowed to remain on the body or the clothes they become hosts for bacteria, and it is the decomposition brought about by bacterial action that gives the objectional odour usually associated with the term 'Body Odour'. Another cause of such smells is the presence of diseased organs.

And with that we come to the main purpose of this chapter: how to ensure that the bodies of the two Tantric partners are always aromatic and sexually attractive to the sense of smell.

We must remember that as the natural odours of the body are not sexually repulsive there is no need to repress the natural secretions. In fact, it would be wrong to do so except where they are visually unaesthetic. By this we mean that sweat suppressors should be used with caution. There is no substitute, however, for frequent bathing, particularly in hot, muggy, climates where the body streams with sweat. If you feel fresh only when you have three or four baths a day you need not use soap for your whole body for every bath: it would be adequate if you were to soap your face, under your armpits, your groin and your feet. The body has a natural layer of protective oils and soap removes this defensive film, but you must get rid of sweaty deposits where bacteria might establish their odour-making colonies. We are told that in every square centimeter of skin there are 30,000 bacteria. We do not know if this is true, but if it is even a quarter true it brings home the importance of skin hygiene. A good Indian substitute for soap is gram flour: it is abrasive, has a mildly pleasant smell and will not harm the skin. It also keeps the skin as clean as the most expensive soap claims to do.

Bacteria also lodge in fibres including human hair. We are firm believers in the hygienic value of depilation: the less body hair you have the less chance there is of you having an offensive body odour. We realise, however, that this general principle must be made subject to the current sexual fashions: if fashion demands that men should have hair on their chests, Tantric males would diminish their sexual attractiveness if they presented a hairless front. But we strongly believe that women should keep their armpits and mons veneris clear of hair. Because of the construction of a man's external sexual organs the depilation of this area might be more difficult to achieve. As for the hair on the head, both men and women should use a good shampoo, frequently. The use of hair dressings is a matter of personal preference, but clean hair has a fragrance all its own.

The mouth is one of the most difficult parts of the body to keep clean. A famous doctor once told us that a person's mouth harbours many more germs than the genital organs: this alone is an excellent reason for scrupulous oral hygiene. Regular brushing of the teeth, morning and night, is not enough. Visits to the dentist are also important because bad breath might arise from decaying teeth and nothing can be more revolting than a sexual partner with halitosis. A sore throat, cough, cold or uncertain digestion can also contribute to a rancid breath. We recommend that you exercise regularly, preferably in the open air, and your private garden attached to your Tantric Room is an excellent choice for an outdoor gymnasium. Exercise in the nude, if possible. You and your partner should also fast once a week during which you should drink plenty of water and fresh fruit juices. We also advise you to go through a regular routine of yogic throat cleaning every time you wash your teeth.

To clean your throat, raise your first and little fingers, bending the second and ring fingers at right angles to the palm. Insert the second and ring fingers into your mouth as far back into your throat as they can go, and then rub your throat and tongue four or five times, spitting out the released mucus. Needless to say, your hands should be very clean before you do this, and your nails should be pared, rounded and cleaned. Do not try to reach too far down your throat at your first attempt: start midway down your tongue and work backwards, reaching deeper into your throat every successive day. If you can insert your fingers as far as they can go after three weeks of practice, without feeling sick, you are doing well.

Now, use the ball of your thumb to rub the top of your throat: that is the upper surface of the lining of your throat.

According to yogis, these two exercises dislodge the dead cells in which bacteria might breed, along with a large number of other odour-causing materials.

The gums should also be cleaned by using your thumb and forefinger to 'milk' them from the jaw end to the biting edge of the teeth, that is, downwards for the upper gums, upwards for the lower gums. This not only massages them, it also helps free them of food particles.

The last area calling for daily attention is the sexual organs.

Men should be particularly careful about their groins. Any suspicion of a rash, pimple or wound in this region should be shown to a competent doctor immediately. If the penis is uncircumcised the foreskin should be drawn back and the head should be washed. If this is not done a cheesy, strongly smelling, white secretion called smegma is likely to collect and lead to irritation and infection besides giving off a most offensive odour. Whenever a man bathes he should wash his penis thoroughly paying particular attention to such accumulations of smegma. The clitoris, too, is likely to get smegma deposits. This secretion should be removed by pulling back the foreskin of the clitoris and cleaning it with a small, damped, swab of cotton. We do not agree with the commonly held belief that the vagina is a self-cleaning organ. It certainly provides a great deal of resistance to bacteria but deposits are likely to accumulate in its warm passage. We also do not believe in douching because a much simpler method is available. Unless the woman has claw-like nails, she should squat on the floor of the bathroom, spread wide her thighs, and clean the inside of her vagina with her fingers, scooping out the excess mucus and other accumulated deposits. After doing so she should wash her vulva thoroughly with a good, mild, foamy soap. No other hygienic steps are necessary except when she is menstruating.

During menstruation we recommend that the Tantric woman should use tampons. If she does not want to buy the expensive, ready-made products she could roll her own from surgical cotton. This has the advantage of allowing the tampons to be tailored to suit the needs: smaller rolls for the beginning and end of the period, larger ones for the days when the flow is abundant. We would also like to remind you that internal sexual hygiene is particularly important during menstruation.

Please also ensure that your undergarments are washed every day and changed even more often if they have been soiled by sweat or other secretions. Synthetic fibres are likely to pick up and concentrate body odours. All garments should be hung up and aired overnight before being cleaned and stored. Synthetic fibre garments should be washed every time they are worn and it is a grave mistake to put them into storage after a mere airing; this is particularly applicable if they have been scented by the perfume used by the person who wore them last. Perfumes stale with prolonged exposure and they might well fix the body odour of the person into the synthetic fibres of the clothes.

Having dealt in great detail with the important matter of sex hygiene and personal odour, we would like to devote the rest of this chapter to the use of perfumes: mankind's way of deliberately creating a sexual aroma.

Perfumes have three purposes: concealing obnoxious odours, neutralizing existing ones, and enhancing personal fragrances.

We do not recommend anyone using perfumes to conceal obnoxious odours. If there is a source of such odours in your body get rid of it by effective hygiene or medical assistance.

Odours are neutralised by the wide range of deodorants. An effective home-made deodorant is lavender about which Dr. Th. Van de Velde, in his excellent and much quoted book **Ideal Marriage** says,

"A good essence of lavender may be compounded as follows: 1 litre of lavender-water, one-eighth of a litre of rose-water (without any musk or other animal substances), and 75 grammes of salammoniae. It can then be tinted a pale blue with phenicine (indigo)."

According to Van de Velde, Camphor and Bitter Almond also serve as natural deodrants.

By far the most creative use of perfumes, however, is for the enhancement of the natural fragrances of the body and to set aromatic moods. Perfumers, all down history, have used certain rules when compounding their scents and every person who wants to use perfumes intelligently should know something about them.

All fragrances start with a natural oil or artificial chemical base. The oils are extracted from flowers, grasses, woods, leaves, herbs, spices: in fact the whole range of vegetable matter. The artificial perfumes, or synthetics, are made from combinations of strongly scented chemicals which have no fragrant equivalent in the living world. The base chosen sets the type of the perfume. There are roughly seven basic types: Single Flower, Multiple Flower or Bouquet, Woodland, Tangy or Spicy, Fruity or Mellow Tang, Exotic or Oriental, and Modern. For instance, **Bellodgia** by Caron and **Muguets des Bois** by Coty are Single Flower fragrances. **Chanel No. 5** by

Chanel and **Blue Grass** by Elizabeth Arden are well known Multiple Flower fragrances. The Woodland category has **Audace** by Rochas, **Vent Vert** by Balmain. We cannot think of a straight Tangy perfume, but Lanvin's **My Sin** can be called a Tangy Oriental. Pure Orientals also seem to be out of fashion but **Tabu** by Dana, and Yardley's **You're the Fire** are excellent examples of this type. Nina Ricci's **Bigarade** and Jean Nate's **Jean Nate** are the only Fruity perfumes we can think of. The last category, the champagne-like, light, dry, Moderns have two famous names in their fold: Revlon's **Intimate,** and Worth's **Je Reviens.** Most perfumes, as can be gathered from this list, fall under the multi-type category, with Carven's **Ma Griffe** clocking in three distinct type-classifications: it is Multi-floral — Woodland — Fruity!

Once the perfumer has chosen the type, it is fixed by minute additions of animal extracts such as the rare ambergris of whales, or the sex-gland extracts of civet cats or musk deer. These do the job of keeping the many fragrances that go into the blending of a perfume, in delicate balance.

Finally, alcohol is added to carry and blend the essential oils and the fixatives.

The addition of the alcohol completes the manufacture of the perfume; all that is left now is to package them in a variety of strengths. Perfumes and perfume oils are the strongest: perfumes have an alcohol carrier; perfume oils, as the name indicates, are carried in oil. Perfumes spread faster, oils linger longer. Next on the gradation, less strong than the perfumes and perfume oils, are the toilet waters with spray mists being toilet waters in spray containers. Colognes are the lightest of the perfumes. Talcums, bath powders, bath oils and soaps are meant to be used as complementaries to the stronger strengths, they have little power or tenacity of their own.

For picking your personal perfumes, and it is best to have more than one, keep a few tips in mind. Everyone has a personal Ph, that is your acid-alkinity ratio, and this will vary with your moods and the temperature. A smoker's skin will not hold a perfume as long as a non-smoker's skin; dry skin will let a perfume evaporate faster than an oily skin; sweat will wash away a perfume and you will have to use some more perfume sooner than you would on a cool day. Hot, muggy, weather is likely to bring out the impact of your perfume far more dramatically than cool, dry, weather; we, therefore, recommend that you wear light fragrances when you are likely to face such tropical conditions.

In the last analysis, the only way of picking your perfumes is by dabbing them on your skin and waiting ten minutes and letting your own chemicals react with them. Do not test more than two or three at any one time because you will only confuse your sense of smell.

Once you have chosen your perfume, never spray it on your clothes because it may stain them. There is also a slight danger that your skin might get discoloured if you dab perfume on it too liberally and then go out in the sun. Also, do not keep a perfume too long or let its container get too hot or too cold: all these might destroy the delicate balance of the oils, fixatives and alcohol and change the fragrance of your perfume.

As for where to use perfume, that's entirely up to your imagination. The usual places are the pulse points: inside the wrists and elbows, behind the ears, at the base of the throat, behind the knees. But remember that you, as a Tantrist, are using it to enhance your sexual impact during the prolonged, and intimate, Tantric contact. We recommend that you bathe in a fragrant soap, use a fragrant talcum, spray the toilet water of your particular perfume on your shoulders, breasts, small of back, stomach and groin: a very light spray on all these places. Then lightly dab the same perfume, in its strongest form, on all the accepted pulse points as well as between the breasts, on the dimple at the base of your spine, and on the inside of the fleshiest part of your thighs.

You may, initially, consider that your Tantric partner is unlikely to come in close enough contact with some of the recommended perfume spots, to appreciate their fragrance. We assure you that this is not so. If you follow the regimen of sexual exercises we suggest, your body will be flexible enough for your partner to get the full impact of your knowledge of sex hygiene and perfumes.

Chapter Six

The Sexual Muscles

By this time you have a fair idea of our programme of Tantric education. Tantra is a total system. It embraces the emotions which are the body's first reactions to stimuli, the psyche which we believe is the source of all aesthetic feelings, the subconscious where all our most primitive yearnings lie, the middle conscious which is the reservoir of our inhibitions, the conscious mind home of logic and awareness, and the physique. All the special qualities of these levels of existence are honed and used to their utmost creativity with the object of projecting the Self into contact with the Sum Totality of all human experiences.

There is, however, one constraint on creativity: the limits imposed by your own ability. You and your partner may want to have a hundred orgasms in a day but your own body is unlikely to be able to give it to you. Similarly, you might want to emulate all the artistic **mithuna** sculptures in Konarak, but your bodies might not be flexible enough, or have enough strength or stamina.

Tantric sex is sustained sex. It is sex prolonged long beyond the normal period of sexual intercourse. Every act of sexual intercourse is, in itself, an athletic feat. In scientifically conducted tests it has been established that in a single act of sexual intercourse the heart beats might rise from 70 beats a minute to an amazing high of 192 beats, the breathing rate might be tripled, the blood pressure soar: all this in under 60 seconds. Every healthy adult has the ability to surge with this burst of athletic energy, but few healthy adults are able to sustain the effort. Male adults are generally 'one-shot' for all their locker-room boasts .... in fact, those who boast most, generally perform least. This one-shot ability is only natural: a single male orgasm pumps out 500,000,000 sperms at every ejaculation, only one is needed to perform nature's task of fertilization. Thus, the survival of the species does not call for more than one shot per mating cycle. But this is not enough for Tantra. In order to achieve the breakthrough that is the essence of Tantra, the sex act has to be prolonged well beyond the normal duration. This, naturally, requires a certain sustained physical effort and the use of muscles which modern men and women seldom exercise. Thus, the first effect of Tantric sex is aching limbs and feeling of great tiredness, unless the bodies of the partners have been toned up and conditioned to the demands that such activities will make on them.

We have, therefore, worked out a system of exercises tailored specifically to develop the muscles that will play an important part in Tantric sex. These exercises will, necessarily, have a good effect on other muscles too, but our claims are limited: if they enable you and your partner to function more efficiently in your Tantric sexual activities, our objects will have been achieved.

Before we describe the exercises, however, we would like to answer a few of the more commonly asked questions.

When should I do the exercises? Whenever it is convenient, but not less than two hours after a heavy meal. When you have a heavy meal your blood is needed by your digestive organs. If you do these exercises at this time, the blood will rush to your muscles and skin and you are likely to get an attack of indigestion or other complaints.

How long should I do the exercises for? Set aside half an hour a day for the first three months and then you can cut it to a maintenance schedule of half an hour a week. In actual practice you are not likely to take more than 20 minutes once you have settled into the routine of it, and your muscles have fallen into the rhythm of the movements.

How strenuous are they? Not very. We believe in the Hatha Yoga dictum that all effective exercises should be done smoothly and easily. Do not jerk needlessly nor work yourself into a streaming sweat. A gracefully executed regimen of exercises which leaves you relaxed and covered in a thin film of sweat is the most beneficial.

What should I wear during the exercises? Nothing if you can help it: remember that when you put the muscles to the use for which you are developing them, you will be stark naked. If you are a man and are worried about hernia wear a pair of swimming trunks if you must, but ask yourself the question 'Am I going to wear a pair of swimming trunks when I make love?'

What should I do after the exercises? Rest for ten minutes. Lie on your back, your hands palm upwards at your sides, in the 'corpse' attitude. Consciously try to relax your muscles by starting from your toes and working upwards, imagining that you are as limp as an old sock. After that it is best to have a warm shower: warm water is most effective in washing away the deposits of your two million pores which will have been working hard to keep you cool during the exercises.

If my partner and I do the exercises together we get so excited that we start making love; what should we do? Make love; after all that is the object of the exercises in the first place. After the initial excitement has worn away you will not have this problem: the excitement arises out of you seeing each other's nude bodies in unusual movements, obviously sex-oriented.

We would also like to advise you to do the exercises in the open air, preferably in the enclosed garden attached to your Tantric Room. If you do not have such a garden, or if the weather is inclement, do them in your Tantric Room in front of a mirror so that you can watch the effect of the exercises on your muscles.

The exercises that follow will warm you, give you increased flexibility, strengthen your back and thighs, and enable you to control the specialized muscles of your genital region.

Trunk bending, front and back. Stand with your legs braced and comfortably apart. Stretch your arms out in line with your shoulders as if you were going to fly. Bend your body forward at the waist as far as you can go without straining. When you reach the limit of your bend flow smoothly into the reverse movement, raising your trunk up. Do not stop when you come erect but continue the movement backwards, that is, bending back from the waist. You will not be able to go back very far and, here again when you have reached the comfortable limit of your back bend start coming erect very smoothly. Pause only when you have completed one set of forward-upward-backward-upward movements. Count one-two-three and start your forward movement again. Do each complete set three times to start with and, even when you are feeling extraordinarily fit, do not do more than six sets. Keep your arms extended all the time except when you have reached the end of a set and are counting three, then you can let your arms hang limply at your sides. Breathe naturally: out when you bend forward and down, in when you straighten and bend backwards, out again when you straighten from the backward position.

Trunk bending, sideways. Stand with your legs slightly apart, your left arm straight down your side, fingers extended along the outer side of your left leg. Your right arm should be bent over your head as if you were pointing to something to the left; the right side of your face lying on the inner side of your right arm, elbow bent into an L, the right forearm resting on top of your head. Bend your body to the left letting the fingers of your left hand slide as far as possible down your left leg. With your head bent to the left, straighten out your right arm till it is parallel to the ground. Hold this position for the count of two, straighten up, reverse arms and bend to the right. Breathe out as you go down, breathe in as you come up. Do each set . . . left, up, right, up . . . three times.

Sitting forward bend. You and your partner should sit on the floor with your legs extended in front of you, toes and soles touching. Bend forward as far as you can, gripping on to your legs to pull yourself down, till you feel a pleasant tension in the small of your back. Come up slowly. Breathe out going down and breathe in coming up. Each set . . . down, up . . . three times.

Prone back bend. Lie face down on the floor. Arch your body backwards, bringing your legs up over your back. Grip your ankles with your hands and then try and pull your legs back putting tension on your arms like a drawn bow. By alternately tensing and relaxing your legs you should, with practice, be able to rock your body backwards and forwards. Rock three times and relax.

The bicycle stance. Lie on your back and thrust your legs straight in the air, supporting your hips on the tripod of your hands and back. In other words, your upper arms should rest on the floor on two sides of your trunk, your elbows bent, your hands supporting your hips. Lock your chin in your throat to get the maximum benefit from this exercise. At first you will find some difficulty in balancing. Get your partner to help you as you should help your partner. After a little practice you should be able to do it with ease. Breathe naturally and hold the position for the count of ten.

Sitting spinal twist. This is a yoga asana that looks far more difficult than it really is. Sit on the floor with your legs stretched out in front of you. Draw up your left leg, bending your knee, keeping the sole of your left foot on the floor. Cross your left foot over your right knee till the outer side of your left ankle is touching the outer side of your right knee. Now twist your trunk to the left, pass your right hand on the outer side of your left leg, reach down and get a grip on your right leg. Try and grip your right leg where the left ankle touches it. If you have done this correctly your right elbow should be braced against your left knee. Your left arm should be curled around your back, palm outward, the fingers resting above the right hip. You will feel your spine tensing. Hold this position for the count of six breathing naturally, and then reverse hands and legs twisting to the right. Do each complete set... left twist right twist... three times.

Prone chest elevation. Lie on the floor, face downwards, forearms and palms pressed flat on the floor on two sides of the chest as if you were going to do push-ups. Raise your palms and forearms from the floor, raise your upper body off the floor as far as you can bend it backwards, your head thrown back so that you look at the ceiling. Breathe naturally and elevate the upper half of your body three times.

The Trunk Rock. Sit on the ground facing your partner. Both you and your partner should spread your legs wide apart letting the soles of your feet touch. Reach out and grasp your partner's wrists while your partner gets the same grip on your wrists. Bend forward while your partner bends backwards. When you have bent as far as you can, start bending backwards, pulling your partner forwards. When you, or your partner bend backwards, try and let the back touch the floor. The movements should be smooth and easy like a see-saw. Breathe out on the forward bend, breathe in on the backward bend. Do the forward-up-backward-up set three times.

At this stage we would like to remind you that it is very important to strengthen the muscles of your back, particularly the small of your back. Yoga considers the spine to be the main communication of the body through which the mysterious Kundalini rises. A supple spine, according to yogis, does much to ward off the effects of ageing.

We now come to the exercises designed especially for the muscles seldom used in modern living but very essential for sexual intercourse. While doing these exercises every male Tantrist should try and raise his penis at the outward thrust, and every female Tantrist should try and tighten her vaginal muscles particularly the **constrictor cunni.** This can be done by squeezing the muscles together as if trying to hold in a bladder or bowel movement.

The Groin Thrust. Stand against a wall so that your heels, buttocks and back touch the wall. The muscles of your buttocks should be relaxed. Now tighten your buttocks and hollow the stomach so that your pelvis thrusts up and out. At this point your buttocks alone should lose contact with the wall. Hold the outward thrust position for the count of three, then relax. You will, naturally, breathe out when you are thrusting outwards and breathe in when you are relaxing and letting your buttocks touch the wall.

While we recommend that you should start this exercise with your back touching the wall, we suggest that you should also vary the position after three days by doing the same exercise from the following positions.

Facing a wall: the action of your groin is the same but here your forehead and chest touch the wall, your toes are slightly away from it, your legs slightly apart, your knees slightly bent. In the outward thrust try and raise your genital area as far up the wall as you can, in the downward thrust try and lower it as far as you can. Remember that the movement should be a movement of your pelvic area alone; do not raise and lower yourselves on your toes to achieve the up and down movement.

Sitting on the Floor with your legs stretched in front of you, your palms resting on the floor just behind your hips.

Lying on your Back with your legs straight in front of you, then with your legs drawn up and bent at the knee, then with your body arched off the ground and only your arms, feet and upper body in contact with the floor.

Lying Supine on your face, flat on the floor, then with your knees drawn up in a crouch, then kneeling on all fours.

Kneeling Upright with your buttocks resting on your ankles.

Supporting yourself against a chair with your hands gripping the seat of the chair and your body at an angle of 45 degrees to the seat as if you were doing push-ups. Also in the reverse position with your back to the chair.

Lying on your side on the floor. It will be clear from our descriptions that we are trying to duplicate the genital movements in all the possible positions of sexual intercourse. In fact, considerable benefit can be derived from these exercises if they are done by the Tantric partners actually getting into the varied positions of intercourse and synchronizing their genital movements without, of course, making genital contact. It must be ensured, however, that the female partner is also allowed to assume all positions, both superior and inferior although these might have little relevance to actual intercourse. In the rear entry position, for instance, the woman might not like to assume the superior position in relation to her male partner. In such cases the partners should exercise independently, but in each other's presence.

The Hula Rotation. This exercise uses most of the genital movements and we recommend it strongly. The Tantric partners stand with their hands clasped behind their heads, their legs slightly separated and bent, and rotate their hips clockwise and then counter-clockwise. The rotation should be done in such a manner that each hip-bone describes a circle in the air, parallel to the floor. Hula dancers describe the same movements with their hips and the Hula Hoop. . . a fad of the '50s and '60s. . . is an excellent device to develop these efficient sexual movements.

Buttock Tightening. Flabby buttocks hamper sexual enjoyment because the partner who has weak buttock muscles can not take part in all the movements necessary to a full enjoyment of the act. These muscles, called the **gluteus maximus,** can be easily brought into condition by tightening. Stand with your legs together, facing each other, palms lightly cupping one another's buttocks. Tighten the buttocks as if worried that someone was going to shove a pin into them. Alternatively, use the trick employed by ballet masters: insert a flat disc gently between the two cheeks. The disc should be about 4 cm in diameter and about a ½ cm thick, and could be made of wood, polystrene or cardboard. An old one rupee coin will also do. The object is to make the buttock muscles tighten and 'hold' the coin for the count of six, and then relax. The Tantrist should be able to feel the toughness and tension in these large muscles.

The buttock tightening exercise can also be done in all the positions in which the Groin Thrust exercise is done. Remember also that when you are tightening your gluteus maximus muscles, the male Tantrist should raise and tighten his penis and the female Tantrist should raise and tighten her vaginal muscles.

The Buttock Walk. An excellent exercise for reducing the size of the hips and buttocks. Sit with your legs extended before you and your hands on your knees. Now tighten your buttock muscles alternately so that they draw you forward on the floor, first on one side and then on the other. Remember to bend your knees slightly as your buttock inches you forward, and then straighten it before you tense the buttock on the other side.

This exercise can also be done with your knees half drawn up and with them fully drawn up so that your thighs touch your chest.

Thigh Movement Exercises. These exercises appear simple but they are likely to make your legs tired when you first do them.

Stand with your legs 25 cm apart. With the weight on your heels, pivot to twist your toes inwards. Pause for two counts. Swing your toes outwards. Do this six times.

Repeat this exercise but as a variation keep the weight on your toes, moving your heels inwards and outwards.

Also do it lying on your back, lying on your face, sitting up with your legs stretched before you.

When bringing the thighs together in this exercise, the male Tantrist should concentrate on raising his penis and imagining he is thrusting it in sexual intercourse, the female Tantrist should imagine she is grasping the penis and 'milking' it with her tightened vaginal muscles.

Thigh Strengthening Exercises. The muscles strengthened in this exercise are the ones you use in scissoring around the body of your Tantric partner during sexual intercourse.

Sit on two chairs facing each other so that the knees of one can be clasped by the knees of the other. Hold on to each other's shoulders, or the seat of the chair. The inner partner should try and separate his, or her, legs and the outer partner should try and press his or her legs together. After doing this for the count of six, reverse knee positions and pressures for another count of six.

The male partner is advised to exercise great care in this exercise because the muscles used in this exercise are likely to be weak, particularly the woman's muscles.

Finally, please be regular about your exercises. If you find you can do them without feeling tired, increase the sets but do them only once a week. And remember to use them in all their variety during your regular acts of Tantric sex.

Chapter Seven

Honing the Senses

In the earlier chapters we have suggested ways to create the right sensuous climate for your Tantric exercises. We have spoken about the Tantric Room, dress, hygiene and perfumes. Here we will go one step further. We shall show you how you can enhance the receptivity of the senses. This is necessary because, in our 'civilized' world our senses have been dulled by a battery of thudding impressions. Smog lies thick and choking over most of the great cities and exhaust fumes and industrial smoke are accepted as a normal feature of life. In food there is decreasing interest in the delicate tastes of rare herbs and flavourings. The gentle textures of silks and cottons have given way to the harsh surfaces of the synthetics. Popular music is judged by its decibel count and its blaring, discordant, harmonies. Subtle shades no longer enrich our art and there is an emphasis on block colours in screaming and un-natural contrasts.

We become aware of creation and communicate with our fellow beings through our senses. A person who is deprived of the use of his senses.... smell, sight, taste, touch and hearing.... might have the physical potential of a genius, but it will remain a potential. He will stay locked in himself, deprived even of the pleasure of dreams and imagination for fantasy must thrust its roots deep into reality and reality cannot exist without awareness. The Awareness of Reality is the ultimate goal of Tantra.

It is for this fundamental reason that we believe that every modern Tantrist will have to relearn how to smell and taste, to touch, hear and see. And that is what this chapter is all about.

To start with we would like you to learn a basic yogic discipline: the method of Shifting the Centre of Consciousness.

Without entering into any arguments about the physical location of the consciousness....if indeed something so supernal can have a location....it is enough
to concede that we act as if our consciousnesses were
located in our heads. But the centre of consciousness
can be moved by a very simple mental exercise. Let
us say that you want to move the centre of your consciousness to the ankle of your right foot. Close your
eyes and imagine that your right leg is growing out of
the top of your head. The right ankle is where the
centre of your skull is, above it is the widening flare
of your calf, your knee, your thigh joining your other
leg at your groin; and beyond, towering above you, is
the height of the rest of your body with your head,
foreshortened by distance, against the blue sky. Hold
this image for a while visualizing your right instep and
toes thrusting out where your eyes and nose are, your
right heel projecting from the back of your head. At
first you will feel a little lightheaded and, possibly, a
little scared, and your picture will blur and fade jerking
your consciousness back to your head. But you will
notice that your right ankle feels warm and tingling.
The greater the warmth and tingle in your ankle the
more success you have had with your consciousness
shifting. Do not give in at the first failure because this
is not a difficult exercise, it is merely an unusual one.
After a few attempts you should be able to hold the
image for a few minutes. That is good enough for our
immediate purposes. You can increase the duration
when you learn more about the science of meditation
in Chapter Nine.

By using this technique you will be able to move the
centre of consciousness to any part of your body. When
you are doing the exercises in this chapter, move the
centre of consciousness to each of the sense organs, in
turn, as we tell you how to hone your senses.

SMELL

If your nose were as sensitive as it is capable of being,
you should be able to distinguish over 2000 different
odours. Perfume blenders can identify very many more

because they have trained themselves to do so; and also because they look after their organs of smell. To start with, then, use a yoga hygiene technique. Whenever you wash your face, cup water in the palm of your hand and, closing one nostril with the fingers or thumb, sniff the water up the open nostril and then blow it out. Do this twice for each nostril. At first you might get a sharp, burning, sensation near the bridge of your nose and your eyes might water, but after doing it for a few days the smarting will vanish. But even when it is smarting you will feel amazingly clear-headed and alert, and you will seldom get colds, catarrh or other nasal complaints.

You are now ready for your sensitivity training.

Collect at least six objects with distinctive, but not harsh, smells. You might, for instance, collect orange peel, a burnt toast, a sliver of delicate soap, a smear of cream, a shred of tobacco, a stick of cinnamon. Space them out on a board and smell them individually, inhaling deeply to get a clear impression of each aroma. When you are quite certain that you can distinguish the different scents, blindfold yourself and tell your partner to turn the board and bring it under your nose. Inhale and identify the objects by their fragrances. When you get a correct score of four, have your partner combine the objects in groups of two, smell them again and try to identify the constituents of each group. When you are able to identify four of the six ingredients, ask your partner to divide one of the groups into two equal parts: the divided group could be split object-wise... an orange-cinnamon group could be split into oranges and cinnamons... or bulk-wise... half the orange-cinnamon mixture to one side, the other half on the other side. Mix these two equal parts with the other two groups. Gargle, clear your nose and, with the blindfold on, identify the ingredients of the two composite groups. A score of four is excellent progress.

Now have your partner draw six spaced circles on the board and rub one of the fragrant objects on each circle, marking the circle with an identifying number. With your eyes open .identify the objects by their smells. After this leave the board out in the sun for twenty minutes and then, blindfolded, ask your partner to move the board under your nose again for you to identify the fainter aromas.

When you have become proficient in these tests, take a walk as soon as the sum comes out after a shower of rain. Make a list of all the smells you have been able to distinguish. Do this as often as you can. You can be proud of your achievement only after you have doubled the number of smells that you recorded on your first aromatic walk on the same route. Resist the temptation to under-record on your first walk because then you will be giving yourself a false sense of progress.

Finally, sit in a low chair and have your partner stand in front of you, leaning over, presenting his or her body for you to smell: cheek, nape of neck, throat, chest, stomach, groin, thigh, calf, wrist, inner side of the elbow, armpit. Blindfold yourself and have the last exercise repeated. Identify areas of your partner's body by memorised scent.

TASTE

Tea tasters, wine tasters, gourmets and chefs all make an effort to develop the discrimination of their sense of taste. You have the potential to be as discerning as these specialists provided you take the trouble to hone your palate.

Clean your mouth, tongue and throat using the yogic hygiene techniques we have described earlier. Chew on a piece of lightly done toast: it should not be darker than golden brown. Rinse your mouth again in chill water.

Using a salt spoon sprinkle a little salt into a glass of water and stir till the salt is dissolved. Taste. If you cannot discern the salt, add a little more, stir and taste. Note how much salt has to be added before you can discern its taste in the water.

Repeat the exercise with sugar. Repeat again with a squeeze of lime.

Keep repeating once a day until you are able to discern half the salt, sugar, lime, originally used.

Now mix the original quantity of salt and lime in one glass, sugar and lime in another glass. Blindfold yourself and try to distinguish between the two glasses and a glass of water without any of these additions. The blind test should be conducted by your partner.

Whenever possible, taste the main flavour-imparting ingredients before they are included in a recipe. Try and locate the individual flavours in the cooked dish.

Make it a practice to try and identify the ingredients in every dish you taste. This is not as difficult as it appears for we have a friend who can do this even though she has not, consciously, tried to develop her palate.

Finally, ask your partner to bathe, using a mild soap, scrub dry and rest naked for half an hour. Then bathe again in water only, without soap, and dab dry. Taste the skin of your partner in the same areas as for the smell test, and try to remember the distinctive flavour of each area. Now sit in a low chair, blindfolded, and have your partner present the same body areas for your tasting and identification.

TOUCH

This is the most widely distributed and the most primitive of the senses. It is also the least used in modern civilization. People today appear to be scared to touch each other as if the sheer contact of bodies will break down the barriers they have erected between hemselves and the world. And they are right. When a person touches another, some sort of primeval understanding seems to pass between them bringing them closer together. Babies deprived of contact with their mothers become retarded regardless of how physically fit they might otherwise be. Lovers have a great need to touch each other in public as if the physical contact reaffirms a bond of understanding against a cold and indifferent world. Later in this book we shall devote an entire chapter to the ego-dissolving technique of stroking that is an essential step in Tantric sex.

The tips of the fingers are among the most sensitive parts of the body and safe breakers, whose unlawful livelihood depends on their delicacy of touch, sandpaper their finger-tips to make them hyper-sensitive. You, too, can heighten the sensitivity of your touch by a few easy exercises.

Collect six objects of varying textures. We use a strip of velvet, a feather, a bit of turkish towelling, a piece of suede leather, a patch of fur, a tender leaf. Look at them and touch them, trying to memorise their textures. Strip and have your partner brush each one of them lightly over your body: the movement should be slow, drifting, graceful. Close your eyes and ask your partner to repeat the exercise. The touch of each object on your body, now, should be as light as possible so that it is only slightly more than a suggestion. Try to identify the objects.

Open your eyes and touch your partner's body. Use tiny circular movements no more than 3 cm in diameter to get the feel of the forehead, cheek, chin, throat, shoulders, and the upper curve of the breast if she is a woman. Blindfold yourself and have your partner place your fingers on those same spots on his, or her, body. Using the same, small, circular movements try to identify the areas touched. Repeat the exercise now touching the stomach, lower belly just above the pubic area, inner side of the thigh, the dimple in the small of the back just above the tail-bone, the spot on the back just between the shoulders and at the base of the neck, the inner side of the biceps.

Remember to keep your circular movements very small: you must judge the place you are touching by the texture of the skin, not from the shape of the flesh in the area.

SOUND

The sense of hearing seems to be a very easy sense to train because you cannot be an efficient musician unless you are able to discriminate between slight variations of sound over a large range. If you have a musical training the further development of your ear will not be difficult, but even if you have no musical knowledge you should be able to train yourself to hear to the full extent of your abilities.

To start with, few people visit their ENT specialists as often as they do their doctors and dentists. The ear is a delicate instrument and it needs a delicate touch. Your body provides a natural lubricant for the ear but when this oily substance dries, and mixes with dust and soap which might have entered the ear, it forms a hard, wax-like substance which might impede your hearing. Do not attempt to remove it with a pin or a matchstick because, if your hand slips, you might make yourself deaf for life. Do not, also, go to any unqualified person asking him to clean your ear: he may infect your ears so badly that you will have to face excruciating agony before they are cured. Such quacks might also cause you to lose your hearing altogether. A yearly visit to a qualified Ear, Nose and Throat specialist is the very least you owe yourself.

Presuming, however, that there is no physical impairment of your hearing organs, start your hearing exercise by recording....or listening to....the sounds of single musical instruments. It would be best if, before doing so, you recorded some chamber music, normally played by three to five musicians. Once you have done so make a recording of the individual instruments played alone. Listen to these solo performances and get a clear picture of the sound personality of each instrument. Now, play the chamber music and try to identify each instrument, following its score throughout the piece In other words you should follow a single instrument at a time as if you were listening to the voice of one friend while a great many other conversations were being carried out at the same time. Once you have been able to follow your chosen instrument throughout the piece, play the music over again and follow another instrument all the way through, and so on for all the instruments.

Do the same thing for an orchestral recording. Conductors are able to listen to the entire orchestra and can still pick out a mistake committed by a single instrument. Choose a fairly prominent instrument such as the French Horn, Violin or Harp, and move on to the lesser instruments as you gain more confidence.

Speak a few phrases softly into a tape recorder and have your partner play it at one end of the room with the volume turned down. Note the volume reading.... or the amount the volume knob has been turned.... when you find the sound is just audible. Close your eyes and concentrate: you know the phrases, you know the order in which they have been said, you know the rhythm of your voice, it should not be difficult to pick out the sentences even though they may be at the limits of your hearing. On the sixth or seventh try you should be able to hear all the sentences recorded by you. Rest and shift the Centre of Consciousness to your ear.....either the right or the left....have your partner turn down the volume a notch, and try to pick up the phrases again.

When you are tired of listening to your own voice, have your partner whisper a few erotic phrases into the recorder. Go through the same exercises but this time it will be a bit harder because you do not know what has been recorded. You are, however, interested in the phrases. The chances are that you will be able to hear them sooner than you expected. Ask your partner to record even more erotic phrases, turn down the volume a notch, and start all over again.

To vary the exercise, go for a walk along a quiet road at night. Make a note of all the sounds you can distinguish. Repeat the walk after two days, at the same hour, and try to add to the number of sounds you can distinguish. Remember that sounds may come to you in an 'orchestration' but, with a little observation, you could break them down into their individual components: your footfalls, for instance, could be broken down into the slight squeak of shoe leather, the crunch of gravel, the grate of an exposed nail on concrete, the slap of your sole hitting a puddle, and so on.

Finally, go into a dark room, lock the door, and listen to the sounds of silence: the beat of your heart, the rustle of your breath, the liquid click as you swallow. Few of us are aware of the sounds our bodies make during the process of living. If we become aware of these life-sounds we will be more aware of our Tantric partner's needs, particularly when we are locked in the ecstasy of sex.

SIGHT

In our civilization, sight has the most erotic impact. Wherever we look....in magazines, on hoardings, in the movies, on the street....erotic images impinge on our conscious and sub-conscious. The clamour for our attention is so great that advertisers have been compelled to resort to harsher and harsher stimuli with the result that our sense of sight is being deadened by the impact of it all. It would appear that we have the latent ability to distinguish 3,70,000 colours but, thanks to the dulling of our perception, this has now been reduced to a mere 70,000. But even so we have not gone as far as the hedonistic Romans went. There are strong grounds for believing that at the height of their power, when world wealth flowed into Roman coffers and entertainers clamoured for the attention of the rich, Roman senses, too, were deadened by excessively gross stimuli. Thus, the people who lived on the shores of the brilliantly blue Mediterranean could not distinguish this glorious colour from the colour of the land around it!

We have not sunk as low as the Romans but we are not very far from it. Unless we do something to halt our decline we will become a race of colourless creatures, able to distinguish only the primary colours Red, Yellow and Blue.

The first step in re-educating the sight is to learn how to rest the eyes, concentrate our vision, and move the eyeballs.

Start by Palming. This is done by covering your eyes with your hands so that the hollows of your palms rest over your eyes and your fingers are crossed over the bridge of your nose, the fingers of one hand covering, and overlapping, the fingers of the other. This is something like the instinctive move a person makes when he does not want others to see that he is crying. If you have Palmed properly, and your extended fingers are tightly closed, your eyes should be in total darkness. Close your eyes under your palms and keep them so for three minutes or slightly longer.

After Palming, open your eyes and blink rapidly six times and then focus them on a small object at the other end of the room: a bolt, a light switch, a nail. Try to see the object as clearly as possible for the count of six then move your focus to the most distant object you can see: a tree, a hill, a car, a flat across the way. Hold this too for the count of six. Then rotate your eyeballs in a clockwise direction....up, right, down, left, up.... three times, and anti-clockwise three times. Blink rapidly. Palm for the count of twenty-four. Do the entire set of exercises three times and end with Palming for five minutes. These exercises activate all the muscles that are used in sight but which we, in our civilization, seldom use properly. Palming also relaxes the eyes as few other things can do.

You are now ready for the awareness exercises.

Three words describe three different qualities of any colour: Hue, Value and Chromaticity. Hue refers to the basic colour: Crimson, Scarlet, Maroon and Pink are all of a Red hue. Value refers to the relative lightness or darkness of a hue: Maroon has a darker value, and Pink has a lighter value, than Crimson, though all belong to the same hue. Chromaticity refers to the intensity of the hue: Crimson and Scarlet are of the same hue and roughly of the same value, but Scarlet has a higher chromaticity than Crimson. Thus, our colour perception is increased by the number of values and chromas we can distinguish in one hue.

Look at a good colour reproduction of an old master: preferably a Vemeer or a Rembrandt. The paintings of Claude Monet also make excellent subjects for our exercise. Now look at a good colour reproduction of a modern painting: preferably a Klee or a Modrian. List the number of colours of various hues, values and chromas you can distinguish in the Vemeer, Rembrandt and Monet. Compile a similar list for the modern paintings. Put them aside for a day and then go over them with a magnifying glass: how many more shades can you find in the paintings? The chances are that you could increase your colour list of the old masters and the Monet by 50%, but that you could add very little to your modern colour list.

Look at the following things in the early morning light, at mid-day, and at sunset:

An old brick wall, preferably moss dappled

An autumn leaf

A tortoise shell of the old polished kind that grandmother used to have at the back of her hand mirrors

A jewel

A green tree.

List the number of colours you can spot in each. Come back to each of them every three days till you have been able to double the number of colours you first saw.

Do the same thing for a candle flame burning in front of a mirror in a darkened room.

Pick up a handful of garden earth and spread it lightly on a sheet of white paper. Take it out into the sunlight and list the different things you see. Come back to it every two days, adding to your list till you have doubled the number of objects you observed at the first sight. The more you look at it the more you will see: sand separates into quartz, mica, shells, black granite; loam becomes tiny seeds, insect skeletons, leaf particles, a flying ant's wing.

Now stand at the top of the highest building you can get to and look around listing the colours you see from your eagle-eye view: sponge masses of trees, grey ribbons of roads, bright beetle-like cars, ant dots of pedestrians, flashing windows, smoking chimneys. Repeat at two day intervals till you have doubled the list you first made.

Finally, check your visual perception by the most important test of all. Ask your Tantric partner to strip and lie down with closed eyes, preferably in the open otherwise in your Tantric Room letting in as much sunlight as you can. Recall the nudes painted by great artists throughout the ages: no one has ever been able to get the exact shades that colour a human body.

Observe your partner's body carefully. At first glance you can distinguish at least seven colours: the darkness of hair, the deep pink of the lips, the pale pink of the nails, the lightness of the thighs, the darker skin tones on the back of the hands, the colour of the eyes, the faint light-catching down on the lower stomach and back. But these are, in a way, the primary colours of the body. There are many subtle gradations in each of them. For instance, the hair on the head is not the same colour as body hair, and even body hair differs in colour value. Artists believe that even the fairest skin has tones of blue, green and yellow in it giving texture to the predominant pink. Moreover these colours change with the light, the mood and the state of the person's health. A friend of ours claims that a healthy body goes through a range of 136 distinct colours between dawn and sunset, more if there are mood and health variations. You might not be able to record so many, but if you can perceive 25 colours in your partner's body in the course of one day, you are doing well. You are also getting an intimate knowledge of your Tantric partner and that will be needed when you do the exercises called for in Chapter Nine.

Which brings us to the end of this group of exercises. We would like you to remember that your Tantric journey is fuelled by the stimuli being fed to your senses. These stimuli must be broad-based to get the maximum impact. Modern civilization has developed an appetite for gross stimuli and, thus, is increasingly deadening its senses and, consequently, demanding even grosser stimuli. If you are to be a successful Tantrist, and live in society, you must constantly guard against such dulling excesses. You can only do this if you take the trouble to sharpen and widen the sensitivity of your senses.

You can never, therefore, let up on the exercises given in this chapter.

Part III

THE TANTRIC JOURNEY

1. Rati and Kama From Kangra
   Painting Himachal Pradesh
   c. 18th Century AD.

2. Anointing From Rajasthan
   Painting c. 18th Century AD.

3: 9. Tantric Asanas. From a
manuscript in Orissa
c. 19th Century.

9

10. Yoni-Asana, From Nepal
    Painting c. 18th Century AD.

11. Chanchalasana, From Nepal
Painting c. 17th Century AD.

12. Janujugmasana, From Nepal
Painting c. 18th Century AD.

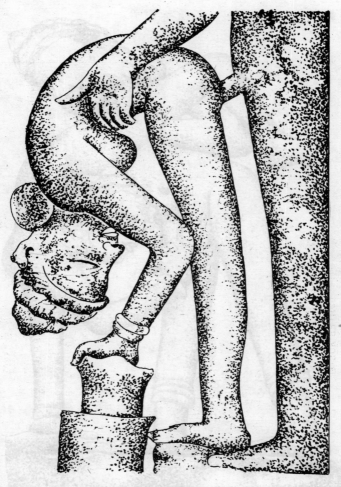

13-14   Naked ascetic coupling with a
Yogini from Lakshmana temple
in Khajuraho.

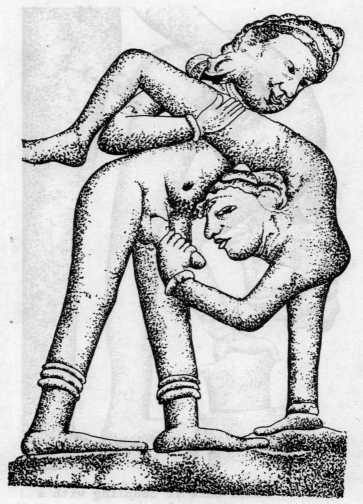

14

Yogini from Chataraana temple in Khajuraho.

15. Icon of Chinnamasta, the
Mahadya from Kangra c 1800

16. From an album painting. Kangra
18th Century.

Chapter Eight

Sexual Awareness, the Duality Concept

We have now come to the most crucial part of this book. Everything that has gone before has been mere background work, a preparation for this chapter and the chapters that follow. You can, at this stage, turn back and the knowledge that you have gained so far will still be of use to you in your normal sex life: you could use the room, the clothes, the sensitivity exercises and the muscular co-ordination to give variety to your love making. But you will not be a Tantrist.

From this moment on, however, you and your partner will be committed to the Tantric way of life and you will find it extremely difficult to turn back. And even if you do your lives will never be the same again. In this chapter we intend to put you through a series of mental exercises that will alter the climate of your mind. We, therefore, suggest that you should first skim over this chapter to get a general idea of what it is about. If your mind revolts against the very concept of Duality, put aside the book for a week or ten days. Take it up again and try to browse over this chapter; if your psyche still shrinks from Tantra, forget it. It is not for you and you will not be able to gain anything from it: in fact it might seriously hamper your present sex life. Human sexuality resides largely in the mind: if your mind is incapable of opening to receive the message of Tantra, then your sex life has a built-in limitation that will be very difficult to remove. We do not say that you lead an unsatisfactory sex life. Far from it. In all likelihood you and your partner are extremely contented with things as they are now. We have reason to believe that Tantra appeals most to those who are discontented with the present state of their love lives. They admit it is great fun and they get a lot of pleasure out of it, but they feel that there must be something more. This is a malady of the creative person: a discontent with the present, a striving for a better future. Tantra is creative sex and it can appeal only to the creative person.

If you and your partner are creative, discontented people....the words are synonymous....then we assure you that the only way that you can open the door to the rich Tantric experience is by accepting the Doctrine of Duality.

No one knows who first conceived the Doctrine of Duality. There have been powerful Phallic Gods and all-pervading Mother Goddesses for almost as long as mankind has been on this earth. But these concepts were just ways of expressing the procreative properties of the earth and the elements; they had little symbolism behind them. In all likelihood our Stone Age ancestors, and their slightly more sophisticated successors, literally believed in their heavily-endowed deities: they did not consider them to be emblems of deeper truths.

But this was not so amongst the seers who authored the ancient Vedic scriptures. Consider some of their achievements:

% In 1500 BC they cast a rustless iron pillar, which still stands in Delhi. No metallurgist today can duplicate it.

% Their Ayur Veda is the most ancient medical treatise in use, and a continuing source of 'modern' discoveries.

% Long before the birth of Christ they laid down such detailed dietetic and hygienic laws that no doctor can fault them today.

% They were the first to discover the atomic nature of matter, give the world the zero, propound the theory of the Pulsating Universe. the latter theory has just been re-discovered by late 20th century cosmologists.

These, then, are only some of the undisputed firsts claimed by the old Hindu scientists; but we have not listed these ancient achievements merely to praise Indian scholarship. That can stand on its own strength. The reason why we have brought these to your attention is to point out that a people who could have made such startling advances in the sciences, so many thousands of years ago, could not possibly have taken their Shiva-Shakti duality concept literally. It was obviously a simple device to express a more abstruse truth. After all, Einstein's brilliant insight into the nature of matter and his years of relentless toil can be expressed in the simple formula $E = mc^2$. No one in his right mind, today, would dream of claiming this to be a magic incantation for the manufacture of an atom bomb: it is merely a simple device for expressing all the knowledge that went into the technology for the conversion of matter into energy. We, with our western upbringing, are used to thinking in the imagery of formulae, hence we can appreciate the significance of Einstein's equation. The ancient Hindus, with their vedic upbringing, were used to thinking in allegories: we must, therefore, appreciate their imagery in their way of thinking, from their point of view.

The allegory of duality says that in the beginning of all creation Shiva and Shakti were united in such complete bliss that they could not distinguish between themselves and thought of themselves only as Shiva. Then Shakti opened her eyes and became aware of herself as a separate entity, though she was still locked in ecstatic intercourse with Shiva. At the next stage they were no longer connected in intercourse but the chains of desire bound them to each other. In the last stage Shakti began to dance and her movements were so bewitching that Shiva mistook each movement of her dance for individual objects quite distinct from himself. And it is this dance of Shakti that creates the illusory world which our senses think is real.

On the face of it this seems to be trivial and rather pointless tale but then most allegories are pointless unless one knows the meanings hidden in them. If we admit, however, that the allegory was made by people who knew a tremendous amount about cosmology and mathematics then we can get some idea of what they were driving at.

Most modern cosmologists believe in the Pulsating

Universe theory. According to this theory all the matter in the universe was once concentrated in a mass the size of a pin-head. No one can even speculate on the properties of this substance: it certainly was not matter, and it could not have been energy. And this incredibly dense substance, this universal pin-head egg, existed in neither space nor time as we know it now. In fact we can only express its qualities in negatives by describing what it was not because we do not know what it was.

Or, to put it in a Hindu way: it was neither action nor inaction, neither light nor darkness, neither matter nor energy, neither positive nor negative. It merely **was**: it had identity and that was all we can be sure it had.

In Tantric imagery it could be expressed as Shiva-Shakti in such close sexual embrace that they could not distinguish between themselves. All they had was identity.

And then, according to our modern astronomers and mathematicians, the 'egg' began to expand and became energy.

Shakti opened her eyes and realised her own identity. To this day a shakti is always considered to be a manifestation of the power or energy of a deity.

As the titanic energy of the exploding 'egg' surged outwards it formed whorls of positive and negative forces, the forerunners of our atoms.

Shakti and Siva separate from their sexual contact, but are still bound by ties of desire.

Atoms formed when tiny negative charges, caught in the tug of a positive nucleus, whirled like planets around a miniscule sun. Most of the atom, the building block of our universe, is empty space. Our senses tell us that matter is solid because they encounter the whirling electrons which travel so fast that they seem to be everywhere at once. In other words, all matter is merely an illusion of the dancing electrons.

Shiva, who is identity or self, is fascinated by the dance of his Shakti and believes that the illusions created by her dance are real.

Viewed in this light, the duality allegory does not

seem to be so trivial or pointless after all. But this is only one explanation and we do not contend that this is the only explanation for the allegory of Duality; we only say that it is one possible interpretation, given the present state of our scientific knowledge. As our knowledge of the universe increases other explanations may be found. But the Tantrist does not wait for scientific explanation to catch up with allegory, he seeks his own explanation by another, older, method. Scientific research follows a one-step-at-a-time system based on vicarious knowledge, experiment and inference. They read what others have done, try to duplicate it, make slight changes in the methods and record their observations. It is a painfully slow process. Tantrists, on the other hand, tap another mental faculty: intuition. Tantrists claim that their sexual disciplines blast through the sub-conscious and make contact with something which has been called the Overmind. Once this has been done the flow of knowledge does not come in little conscious packets of logical sequence, it overwhelms the searcher's mind in an ecstatic totality of awareness: in fact, the word 'Tantra' is derived from the sanskrit root word 'tan' meaning expansion.

We have often been asked why Tantra relies so heavily on sexuality. We believe that there are three reasons for this. Firstly, the trancendental experience of sex is something that most normal people can relate to: it is a form of discipline which carries its own rewards without veering from the basic duality concept. You do not need to have a markedly philosophical bent of mind to appreciate the fundamental duality of sex, and from that admission it becomes all that much easier to appreciate the concept of Universal Duality. Secondly, sexual intercourse does, in some yet unexplained way, open the door to the sub-conscious, though it is normally for a very limited time. This should be clear from the conduct of lovers who are deeply, sexually, involved with each other: they say and do things which would horrify or disgust them in any other situation. Finally, it is only in the highest sexual ecstasy that the lovers' identity barriers dissolve and they act as primal Male and Female and, eventually, merge in a mindless ecstasy that dissolves even their sexual identities. At that peak of orgasm, or the instant before it, your interests and those of your partner are so identical that you are not conscious of yourself as a man or a woman but only as an identity rapt in the ecstasy of sex. Tantra believes that in this fleeting orgasmic moment you have glimpsed the oneness of the universe: a bliss which Zen calls satori and Christianity calls the beatific vision.

We have tried, at some length, to express the philosophy of Tantra in terms which would make it relevant to the modern western mind. We realise, of course, that there are great limitations to this method. Christian religious painting, sculpture and music all expressed identical themes, within a certain stylised and limited idiom, and to people who shared a common cultural heritage. And yet it would be impossible to convey the sensory and intellectual impact of Handel's Messiah in either stone or canvas. Tantra and western science are far more disparate disciplines than music on the one hand and fine arts on the other.

Nevertheless, in spite of the mutually divergent nature of the two systems, we have tried to explain one in terms of the other before asking you to undertake the first series of mental exercises. These are not traditional Tantric exercises because Tantra evolved in civilizations which had already accepted the Dualistic principle. These exercises have been specifically tailored for the western mind and we have tried to make the transition, from one way of thinking to the other, as gentle as possible. From childhood your mind has been trained to move from one logical step to the next. We have to train it to relax and open to the flood of impressions that is the Tantric way. There are many methods of achieving this. One is by forcing the mind to open under the bludgeoning impact of drugs and there are many people for whom this system works well. But for most of us such drugs are dangerous. When the unprepared mind suddenly finds itself defenceless against the invasion of a myriad bewildering impressions it is much worse than the traumatic experience of a young girl being gang raped. The mind tries to flinch and hide but it cannot escape and so something which should be an ecstatic experience becomes stark horror. Some call it a bad trip; in an older vocabulary they called it possession by devils. Zen tries another way to cause the mind to surrender. It subjects the student to **koan**, logically insoluble riddles. There is, for example, no logical answer to the **koan** "A girl is walking down the street, is she the younger or the older sister?" When your logically-oriented mind has become exhausted trying to solve the riddle, you will give up and surrender. You will then, hopefully, learn to open your mind and accept impressions without the constraints of logic.

These are two methods. We have chosen a third. We have tried, by offering the mind the reward of sexual stimulus, to teach it to accept the existing reality beneath creation. If your mind learns to accept the inflow of Tantric impressions offered by our first set of mental exercises, then you will have achieved much in your Tantric quest. But if, in spite of our efforts, you find your mind flinching from some of the exercises in this chapter, remember that the gap to be bridged is vast. We have tried to do our best in the time and space available: the rest is up to you.

The 1st Exercise. Your mind is most receptive when you are lying in bed, relaxed, and just before you fall asleep. Make sure that you are not extremely tired, worried, sick or under the controlling influence of alcohol or drugs, before you start this first exercise. If you are relaxed and happy with your sexual partner start your mental exercise whilst you are still buoyed up with the glow of orgasm.

Lie back and let your mind drift. Imagine that you are lying naked in a boat, on a warm summer's day, drifting down a cool and pleasant river. See the sky above, with the occasional puff of white cloud, and the branches of overhanging trees slipping past. Hear the sound of water lapping on the sides of your boat and the soft drone of bees in the flower-covered fields through which the river runs. Smell the soft fragrance of flowers against the green, watery, smell of the river. Draw the fragrances into your lungs and taste the subtle flavour of them on your tongue and palate. Feel the breeze over your body, the warm and cool bands of sunlight and shadow, the rough boards of the boat under you. Now, when the scene is firmly in your mind and you can feel the weightless drifting of the boat, imagine that your sexual partner is lying nude in your arms while you drift in the boat. Don't move your hands to feel your partner's body but become aware of your partner through your senses: the touch of skin and hair and flesh on your naked body, the fragrance, the taste, the sounds of breathing. You might find a slight stirring of desire with the vividness of your thoughts. Let it come but do nothing about it. Make your excitement part of the sensual feel of the scene and drift, drift drift till you fall asleep. . . .

It should take you between four days to a week to get this picture stabilised in your mind. You must follow the same general sequence every day, though, once the picture assumes an existence of its own, the scene will vary slightly. But no other person should intrude on the scene: it is your river protected by fences or distance from all other human intrusion, and you must not think of how you boarded the boat, or how you will get out of it, or where the river leads to. Keep the scene as we have described it, unquestioning, relaxed, contented.

The 2nd Exercise. When the drifting sequence has been firmly established in your mind, try returning to it whenever you are relaxing. At first you should attempt it only when you are alone and reasonably unworried: in your office, while you are waiting for an appointment, at home. It will not be necessary to lie down, but you should have your spine fairly straight though not rigid. Later, when you can conjure up the drifting sequence whenever you want to, try using it to bring on relaxation: use it when you are worried and want to recharge your psychic batteries. The erotic content is very important and both you and your sexual partner must appear in every sequence, and you must bring all your senses to bear on the scene. It is not enough merely to picture it: you must also smell, taste, touch and hear it as vividly as possible. If you are a man you will soon learn how to control an erection by keeping the erotic element within the limits of your physical control. Again, it is likely to take you between four days to a week to get this exercise stabilised.

The 3rd Exercise. You are now ready to learn how to look at and enjoy your own body. Go into your Sexual Room when you are certain that you will not be disturbed for at least half an hour. Close the doors, draw the curtains and switch on the light. Strip and sit facing the mirror with your back straight, your stomach comfortably taut, your legs spread apart, breathing deeply but naturally. Now look at yourself frankly and without shame. Consider that you are not looking merely at yourself, a person, an individual; believe that you are looking at the personification of your sex, Man or Woman, Adam or Eve. Mentally step back from yourself, as it were, and imagine that you are a voyeur looking secretly over your own shoulder, admiring the nude body displayed in the mirror. Imagine that you are speaking into a microphone describing what you see. You are a disembodied spirit, an invisible visitor from another planet, sending back a report on the only specimen of Male or Female Homo sapiens you, or your race, have ever seen. Be frank, uninhibited, critical, admiring, appreciative, sensual. If you would like to mate with such a creature, say so. If you would like to touch the creature say so, and do it, describing all the while. If you get a stir of passion at your touch, revel in it and describe your feelings. Sensitive or imaginative people might be tempted to masturbate: don't do it. Not because it is wrong: it is neither right nor wrong. Don't masturbate because that releases your sexual tension and from now on you must try to maintain your sexual tension as long as possible. If you have done the second exercise properly you will have learnt to keep your imagination in check. In your verbalised report you could say "I am longing to place my hand on that hard, erect, phallus", or, "My hand feels drawn towards those beautiful breasts", and then add, "But if I do what I want to I shall destroy the beauty of this creature vibrant with passion". This sequence sounds absurd in cold print but it is amazingly effective in re-establishing control, and every time you establish control over these urges you are that much closer to the goal of total orgasmic control. If necessary, keep a flask of cold water at hand. If you find you cannot hold yourself in check much longer, drink two glasses of water. The change in pace and the breaking of the mounting tension, more than the water, helps restore your equilibrium.

The object of this exercise is to make you totally familiar with your own body without shame or diffidence. There are very few people who can view their bodies with frankness, and fewer still who can conjure up a picture of themselves nude... You must learn to do this whenever you need to. Test the accuracy of the memory of your body by the next exercise.

The 4th Exercise. Now, when you picture yourself and your partner in the drifting sequence, make a slight change in the scenario. If you are visualising the drifting sequence in office take the scene one step further and have the river flow through the office. Stop the boat and step ashore amidst the tables and typewriters, secretaries and visitors. Everything in the office is exactly as it should be except you. You are stark nude. And now, in great detail, imagine the reactions of all those present. Again you must be as graphic as possible, bringing all your senses into the scene: the horrified looks, the falling chairs and screams, the smell of perfume as a secretary rushes past, the flavour of the tea or coffee being brewed, the feel of the clothes of the people who brush by you. Introduce an erotic element, by all means, but don't dwell on it. In fact, when the panic is at its height, step into the boat and resume your interrupted drifting, leaving the office and its turmoil far behind. Always finish this fourth exercise as you started: drifting on the placid river far from the eyes of other humans, timelessly, endlessly, peacefully......

If, during the 4th exercise, you find it difficult to visualise your own body in any of its details, do the 3rd exercise again as soon as possible. As a general rule you will have to do both exercises side by side: one at home, the other in office. It should take you about a week to get your visualisations image-perfect.

The 5th Exercise. The script of this is the same as that of the 4th exercise, but now you must give yourself the power to see through the clothes of all the people you encounter in the office. As you step ashore, nude, and the people express varying degrees of dismay and amazement at your appearance, switch on your X-Ray vision and strip them. This step of the exercise is not as easy as it sounds. Remember that you are trying for complete realism within the limits of your seenario. You will, at first, be tempted to over-endow the opposite sex, under-play your own. Avoid this. Before you proceed to this step in the exercises, study your colleagues carefully and try and see beneath the disguises so many of us wear: the padded shoulders, cinched-in waists, painted over scars. Thanks to the casualness of modern dress the task is much easier now than it might have been a few years ago. Many of the women prefer the bra-less or the natural look; the men rely more on exercise than on their tailors to keep them trim. Nevertheless, there are still a large number of subtle deceptions in hairstyle, the cut of clothes, the manner of walking. Try and penetrate these camouflages to get to the person beneath. Make your stripping look a matter of habit and you will soon find yourself seeing things that most people miss: the flash of a thigh as a normally demure woman sits, a glimpse of deep cleavage when she leans over, the outline of her panties as she climbs into a car or up a flight of stairs, the short hairs on a man's arm, the jut of his crotch, the subtle way a man's pupil's widen when an attractive woman comes in sight. But, once again, when you have viewed your naked colleagues in their panic, return to your boat and drift away as you had done before......

The 6th Exercise. Your mind is now ready to view the entire duality of nature. You have trained yourself to see through the ineffective disguises of clothes and observe the naked people within; extend this awareness to the whole world. Become a voyeur of the sexual truths of creation. Nothing is neuter, nothing is dead.

Everything that is inflowing, fissured, rounded, soft is Feminine; rainwater flowing down a welcoming gutter, a crack in the earth, the warm curve of a light bulb, the caress of the breeze on your cheek. Everything that spouts, thrusts, angles, abrazes is Masculine; an erect fire hydrant gouting its water into the street, the implacable plunge of a pile driver, the gear lever of a high-powered car, the virile harshness of rusted iron. With the sexually aware mind of an adolescent seek the womanliness in every woman, the manliness in every man, and personify them in the world around you: the bole of a tree curved like a neighbour's hip, bobbing balloons as resilient as a sun-bather's breasts, towering thunderclouds as dominating as a lover standing over a bed, a nylon carpet as bristly as the hairs on a surfer's chest. Keep a diary to record your sexual impressions and share them with your Tantric partner. You will not only sharpen your awareness by such sharing, you will also grow closer together and find your impressions merging as you view the world with your own, secret, exhilarating, vision. You will both be staggered, enbarrassed, as your primitive minds break through and show you creation as it really is. Colours, sounds, smells, tastes and the feel of things take on a new vividness and you will catch yourselves smiling for no other reason except the excitement of being alive. All Tantrist live in a bubbling, never-ending, Spring Fever, in love with the world and everything in it, alive with the driving, sexuality of all creation.

If you have come with us so far you will have realised that, to a Tantrist, it makes no difference whether a person or thing is sexually available: it is not the availability that is seen by a Tantrist, but its essential nature. You can appreciate a great work of art for its intrinsic worth without any thought of possessing it. Tantra does this for the sexual duality of all creation. The worth of anything in Tantra is the extent to which it personifies Maleness or Femaleness. This is the one touchstone and this is all that you have to train your mind to look for. the sexual beauty of everything around you. You will be shocked, at first, with the revelations of your mind; learn to live with it, encourage it. The shock is merely the reaction of your middle mind, starched with the phobias and prohibitions of society. It does not like being bypassed, but unless you learn to bypass it you will never be able to share the ecstasy that is your right. Keep watching for the shock reaction. It is only when you have learnt to overcome it, it is only when your mind accepts the search for duality as the natural view of creation, it is only then that you will be ready for the next step.

Chapter Nine

Meditation for Sexuality

You have learnt to open your mind to the sexuality of all creation. Now you must enter an even stranger place: the universe of your mind. It will be an awesome experience.

Yoga believes that the mind is like a whirring wheel, spinning random thoughts, and the more you try to hold it the more it spins with the pressure of your efforts. Like the observer in the quandary of Relativity, the very fact of observation imposes its own distortion on the object observed. The only instrument we have for observing the mind is the mind itself, but the mind is indisciplined and spinning and how can a thing that is indisciplined impose a discipline on itself? It seems to be a problem that has no solution but a solution has been found and it starts with a reduction of sensory inputs during meditation.

There are five major disciplines the beginner in meditation has to adhere to. These are, always meditate:

> Alone
> In the Same Comfortable Posture
> In the Same Place
> For the Same Length of Time
> Every Day

To these you must add the two minor disciplines These are, when you meditate try and do so:

> In the Same Dress
> Under the Open Sky or Where a Mirror Gives
>   the Illusion of Space

You do these to make habit work for you; to establish a distraction-excluding discipline: 'I dress in this way, at this time, and go to this place and sit in this manner every day.' Once the pattern is established the mind will tend to fall into its meditative pattern effortlessly in the same way that the digestion falls into the hunger pattern at established meal times, and the eyes begin to close at established sleep times. We also recommend that you meditate in the open air, if possible: on the banks of a lake, on a hill top, at the edge of a forest, overlooking a plain. The greatest meditative thinkers have always retired into the wilderness before commencing their teaching life and, to this day, Indian savants seclude themselves in caves in the high Himalayas in order to lead a richer, more creative, mental life. But if you cannot find such a place, your Tantric Garden or Tantric Room will serve the purpose. In your Tantric Room you should sit before a mirror to get the illusion of depth.

Having entered your meditative place, settle yourself down comfortably, breathe deeply to fill your lungs with oxygen and clear your body of fatigue-building poisons, and then settle down into a relaxed rhythm, closing your eyes. You are now ready for the meditative exercises.

Your first meditative exercise will be:

FOLLOWING THE STREAM OF CONSCIOUSNESS

When you close your eyes and see the darkness before you, fill it with a sense of openness, awareness and peace. Imagine that you are suspended effortlessly in the air over a vast plain, now it is covered in the darkness before dawn but you know that soon the sun will rise and you will see it stretching before you: fields and lakes, a meandering river, distant trees and, on the horizon, a blurring range of mountains. Become aware of the details of the scene lying in the concealing dark: the wind blowing over the grass of the great plains, the shimmer of the river, the glisten of the lake, the cloud-reaching haze of the hills. Sense the untrammelled openness of the landscape where your thoughts and your will can drift as freely as a wisp of thistledown. Let the peace of it flow into you suffusing you like a perfume. Soon you should be filled with a great feeling of joy and tranquillity. Hold this euphoria for a while and then draw yourself, smiling, away, as if to a greater height and let the scene drift away from your mind. Slowly, the stream of consciousness will begin: emotions first, probably, leading to remembered situations, followed by more emotions and the faces connected with them giving rise to plans and schemes and elation blossoming into vivid pictures of yourself in a heroic situation getting the adulation of the crowd and still more elation and pride......

This account has been based on an actual experience which we shall describe to give you some idea of how the stream of consciousness ignites one idea from another in a mental chain reaction.

'Joy and tranquillity and drifting, drifting, drifting on the river under the sun-dappled willows   striking the ball for a six across the glare-filled pitch and the faces going wild with excitement   as I stride across the oval, the bat tucked under my arm and a mean expression darkens the face of the Aussie he's a mean one but when the ball comes rocketing down the emerald green strip I'll be ready   smack! there it goes soaring over the steeple while the crowd roars   as I shake the Dukes' hand   President's hand in the painted Room   the TV cameras whirrr the commentator's voice filling the homes of India and everyone, everyone, everyone is proud of me thinking of me   happy for me'

The gaps marked the change from one thought to the next but, as anyone who has watched his stream of consciousness can confirm, there is no gap between one thought and the next: very few sequences of thought come to a logical conclusion because they give rise to new ones before they can be concluded, like the colours of the rainbow merging imperceptibly into each other. It is possibly this flowing character of the stream of consciousness that gives rise to the confused nature of dreams when we try to fit them into a logical framework during our waking consciousness. And we must impress upon you not to try to influence or change your stream of thought, do not get involved with it. Stay aloof from the kaleidoscoping pictures like some grey, smiling, Buddha sitting on a cool hill while your thoughts flow vividly below.

For this is the power of the mind that we must learn to use to control the mind: its remarkable ability to sit back and watch itself work.

This first meditative exercise teaches you to relax and draw yourself away from the chaos of your thoughts without being either touched by them or having them touch you. When you are able to achieve this aloofness from your everyday self you have won the first battle in thought control; but you still have a long way to go.

The next step in your mind control regimen is:

SINGLE POINTED CONCENTRATION

In this exercise, which should be attempted only after you have achieved what you set out to do in the Stream of Consciousness discipline, you try to increase your powers of concentration of focusing your mind on a single object till it fills your entire conscious mind.

Hold your palm in front of you. It is best for you to rest your hand on something so that it will not get tired while you look at it. Remember to keep your spine straight. It is always best to keep your spine straight during meditation because not only is this the recommended yogic posture, it is also the most comfortable one for long periods. Keep your palm as far from your eyes as you would a book that you were reading.

Now look at your palm as an integral whole. Do not distinguish between the lines and the fingers, at first, or between the ball of the thumb and the whorls of the finger-tips. View the palm as a complete creation, a whole universe, in itself. Your palm **is** the universe: it contains all the stars and the planets, all the spinning atoms and the mysterious seas where unknown monsters lurk and the great ranges of mountains so that even the Himalayas are less than the height of the ridges of your skin and the hollow centre can contain a million island universes with a billion stars each with their attendant planets on each of which lies a teeming world of plants and animals and men who, in turn, have palms at which they are looking and seeing all the stars and the planets, all the spinning atoms and the mysterious seas where unknown monsters lurk and the great ranges of mountains so that even the Himalayas are less than the height of the ridges of the skin and the hollow centre can contain a million island universes with a billion stars each with their attendant planets on each of which lies a teeming world of plants and animals and men who, in turn, have palms at which they are looking and seeing all the stars and the planets......

When you find yourself getting lightheaded with the spiralling corridors of your thought, draw yourself back, breathe deeply, and start concentrating again on a green leaf, focusing your attention on it to exclude all else so that it forms the entire universe on which you live.

When you know that you can hold your concentration with unwavering attention for six to ten minutes, go into a darkened room, light a candle before a draught-free mirror, and cencentrate on it. But this time extend your concentration to embrace the air around the candle: the shimmering patterns of heat, the faint scent of the burning grease, the weightless weight of the flame, the microcosmic roar of the consuming fire. See the invisible shimmer, smell the incandesence, feel the weight, hear the roar. Let the flame fill your senses with its presence. Merge with the flame, become the flame so that it flares around you and you are the flame and the flame is you, your life, your timeless force burning through time, changing over countless forms but always the same, always the burning flame......

If you have succeeded in doing this last exercise, you have taken your first step in projection: feeling an empathy with an object outside the framework of your body. It is easy to shift your centre of consciousness to a part of your own physical structure, but you have now shifted your eentre of consciousness to the flame. This is the first step in telepathy but, we hasten to inform you, we are not qualified to teach you such powers in all their strength. It is enough for our purposes if your mind is able to empathise with an inanimate, and external, object. We shall come back to the logical extension of this exercise a little later in this chapter.

We shall now show you how to give force, and expression, to your concentration by introducing you to:

MANTRA AND JAPA YOGA.

All creation is vibration: a block of granite is vibration, a pinnacle of ice is vibration, a moonlit lake is vibration, the wind in the pines is vibration, music is vibration, thought is vibration, love is vibration. The whole of creation is vibration hanging shimmering in time. Everything can be expressed in vibration. Learn to express the passion for your Tantric partner in vibration.

Break up your partner's **name into** *its* syllables and pronounce each syllable as a chant of vibration. **Eeeeeee** should be high-pitched and aimed to stir the top of your skull. Tibetan Tantrists use this sound when they seek to pierce the head to release psychic forces. You should actually be able to feel the tingle at the top and centre of your head when you make this sound. **Ayyyyy** fills your throat with vibration and when you pronounce this vowel in its chanted form your throat should feel full with the richness of the chant. **Ahhhhh** is perhaps the richest of the single sounds because it resounds from the echoing hollowness of your chest. Feel the warmth of the vibration of this note, as you chant it, filling your chest with its timbre. Direct your attention to your hips when you make the sound **Oooooo** and, if you are doing it correctly, you should be able to feel a tremulous quiver tingling your pelvic arch. The **Mmmmmmmm** and **Nnnnnnn** sounds set up vibrations in the entire skull: jaws, ears, back of the eyes, brain case, till the entire bone structure of the head seems filled with resonating sound, almost raising you up. Thus, the mystic mantra **Om,** when chanted in the correct way, sets up vibrations along the entire body from the pelvic arch to the brain case and brings the entire Self of the person in harmony with the ultimate sound, the Word, of all creation.

There is also another meditative science which we would like to combine with mantra: it is the discipline of repetitive sound known as Japa Yoga. Science has only just begun to grope for the explanation behind the awareness-opening possibilities of this strange yoga: faith and intuition, however, have been aware of its beneficial effects for centuries. All faiths, all down the ages, have laid considerable stress on repeating certain holy names and phrases over and over again.

Sit in your contemplative posture before the flame and, after you have excluded all other thoughts but the flame, start chanting the name of your Tantric partner giving each syllable the full value, focussing the power of the syllables on the various parts of your body. The name must be extended for the duration of one full breath, each syllable being given equal time. Inhale when you have finished chanting the name and repeat your chant again and again and again.

When you first start chanting, verbalise the syllables clearly giving each its full resonant value; later, start by chanting the name but, after you have done so ten times, chant it in your head for the rest of each meditative session: the duration of each chant should coincide with the beat of your heart till it becomes an effortless, subliminal thing and almost a part of the rhythm of your life. Keep repeating the chant mentally whenever you relax or have a spare moment. You will find that you are not taking up the chant but merely becoming aware of it being chanted subconsciously in your mind. When you reach this stage you will realise that you have begun to tap reservoirs of calm and serenity that you did not know existed in you. This simple yogic discipline is the basis of Trancendental Meditation, and we could easily stop here and leave you feeling on top of the world. But there is still one more meditative discipline left before you can take the next step on the Tantric path.

We refer to:

PERSONIFICATION

This final meditative exercise presumes a mastery of

all that has gone before, unless you have a vivid, and intimate, knowledge of your Tantric partner's body you will make no progress in this discipline. You must not only be able to conjure your partner's body in all its sensual impact....sight, smell, taste, hearing and touch....you must also be able to hold the image clearly for a sustained length of time. Initially, therefore, it would help if you have a full-length photograph of your Tantric partner, preferably in colour and in the nude. If you can play a recording of your partner's voice and smell something evocative of your partner, the sensual impact will be further enhanced. Have all this in hand in your Meditative Place before you enter it. Also have a candle in front of the mirror, ready to be lit. And then, after all this has been arranged, charge yourself full with the force of the Dualistic Vision till you are brimming over with the driving sexuality of all creation.

Now, when your mind hums like a dynamo charged with sexual stimulus, you must consolidate and control it. It will be whirring now: confused, over-excited, bursting its self-imposed barriers of restraint. Do not be worried because that is the state in which it must be to get the full benefit of this meditation.

Enter your Meditative Place, close the doors and windows, strip and sit comfortably before the mirror, your back straight. Light the single candle in front of the mirror and switch off all other lights. If you are meditating in the day, exclude sunlight from the room. If you are meditating at night, make sure that no external light enters the room. The only light falling on your nude body should be from the candle in front of the mirror.

Breathe easily and look at your naked body frankly and uninhibitedly. Remember how you looked at it during an earlier exercise, as if you were an interested alien looking at it from over your shoulder. Look at it that way now. Admire it, criticise it, yearn for it, be proud of it as the body representing every single member of your sex that has ever lived, or will ever live, in this world.

When your senses have been stirred by your self-adulation, gaze at the flame. It should be in front of you and slightly lower than eye level. Look at the flame and fill your mind with it: its shape, texture, colour, light and shade. A flame is one of the most beautiful symbols of the sexual power locked in you: the power that you have now stirred by looking in love at your naked body sitting triumphantly in front of the candle-lit mirror.

Now draw the image and its meaning into you and close your eyes, holding it in your mind as if you had plunged into the heart of the flame. The living fire surrounds you, bathing you, wrapping you in the flaming heart of a creation which throbs with sexuality. Feel the image with all the force of your imagination. You are the flame, the flame is you. Your gross, material body has been burnt away and only the real You is aflame now: soaring, living, bright, changing, eternal. And the force of it, the essence of it is drawn from the very essence of creation: the fire of sexuality.

Hold the reality of the image as long as you can and then relax, letting it fade away.

Do this at least once a day, after your mind has been stimulated with the sexual images of the world outside, till the flame is burnt into your mind as the living symbol of the sexuality of the world. When you can plunge into the flame after a few seconds of looking at it, place the picture of your partner near the candle, hold your partner's perfume near your nose. . . . a scented garment would be best. . . . and turn on the recorder playing your partner's voice, preferably whispering erotic words to you. And then take up the chanting of your partner's name, not merely in your mind, but in sound, giving each syllable the full value of its vibrations. Modulate the chant to merge with your partner's recorded voice and the fragrance that is evocative of your partner. You will find that your voice can continue the chant freeing your mind to think its own vivid thoughts. Think first of the sexuality of the world, the duality that has stirred your senses; merge this duality with the most erotic images of your partner that you

can imagine.... moving, writhing, demanding, giving...
and draw both these merged images through the flame
till the flame becomes the body of your partner which,
itself, is the synthesis of all the eroticism of the world.
Make the flame burn and throb with the aroused body
of your partner, all the while chanting your partner's
name, the recorder playing your partner's voice, your
nostrils assailed with your partner's scent.

The flame flickering before the mirror should now fill
your entire universe, capture your entire perception, and
in the centre of the flame, absorbing it and being absorb-
ed by it, is your partner changing with the changing
flame, as luminous with sex and desire and yearning as
the flame is. Your partner and the chanted name now
fill all creation and there is nothing else but this bright
all-consuming, thing resonant with its own chanted name.

Now take the greatest leap of all: move your mind
closer and closer to the flame. You have had some earlier
practice but now you must move into a flame which is
already occupied and you must merge not only with the
flame but with personality burning unconsumed within
it. See the flame which is your partner enlarging, becoming bigger and bigger till only the dark centre is
clear to you and its curved luminous wings spread to the
corners of the universe. Shift your Centre of Consciousness to the centre of the flame which is the centre of
your partner which is the dark, creative centre of the
universe.

With the chanted name of your partner filling the
chambers of your Being, draw yourself into your Flame-
Partner, merge into each other, absorb each other repeating the name all the while till it throbs hypnotically
with the beat of your heart, the breath of your lungs, till
the name and the image in the burning flame become an
integral part of your echoing endlessly in the corridors
of your mind...

We would like to issue a word of warning before we
close this chapter. These meditative exercises are extremely personal and designed to help you and your Tantric
partner merge your personalities. The nature of the exercises is such that they must be done individually. Be-

cause of this, it is difficult for one partner to keep track of what the other partner is doing; and this is where the danger comes in. These exercises give one partner an almost obsessive preoccupation with the other: very necessary for the next ego-dissolving exercise of Tantra. But the preoccupation must be mutual. The male partner must be as committed to the female partner as she is to him. If there is an imbalance of commitments on either side, one partner might get disgusted with the devotion of the other and wish to break off the relationship This is a very natural reaction and, regrettably, we know of no way in which this can be overseen and controlled by a third person.

We, therefore, strongly advise both partners to maintain a constant dialogue about their progress in these meditative exercises. Question each other, probe, exchange experiences and make certain that both are moving at the same pace. If one is ahead of the other the leading partner must wait till the tardy one has caught up. Make use of the questionnaire to re-establish parity of outlooks because, as a result of these exercises, the sexual approach to life of both partners is likely to undergo a radical transformation, but it is not certain that the changes will run along parallel lines: guard against any divergence. Also resist the temptation to pretend that you are making more progress than you actually are: it often happens that the most gifted people are the slowest to make apparent headway because theirs is a deep-rooted change and not merely a superficial soaring. Do not be ashamed to admit the doggedness of your pace, and do not be scared to probe the claimed pace of your partner. If you find that your partner is rushing to experiences that you have not had, caution him or her against such flights of fancy because the chances are that wishful thinking has played a great part in the rapid advancement claimed by your partner.

The involvement that these exercises create is much closer than any physical merging of bodies. Physical merging, at best, is never more than a mere embracing, with a very limited interpenetration. Mental involvement, however, knows no barrier. In its final form it becomes a total commitment, a complete identification of one personality with another. You must, therefore, ensure that the involvement is always, every time, and in every way, mutual. There must never be any imbalance of commitment.

From now on it will be our aim to obliterate your individual selves so that a greater, merged, Self will be released. This is a frightening thought to those who do not know Tantric beliefs: the ego is normally something to be clung to with an insane possessiveness. But Tantrist know that to lose your ego is to find it. To lose your limited ego is to find your Greater Ego: time-spanning, creation-embracing, self-merging with your Tantric partner.

For when you and your partner have completed these contemplative exercises we shall bring you together again for an experience which will give you a degree of joy that you could never have experienced before.

Chapter Ten

Stroking

We firmly believe that the future of civilization lies not in an increase of material goods but in a deepening of our awareness of the world. We must learn to look at the world as if it were an integral part of us. As if every leaf that stirs, every animal that whimpers, every person's pain and pleasure, effected us personally. This has been the constant message of all great thinkers, all great religions, and unless we enrich our appreciation of the world we will never advance.

The key to the future of mankind is Empathy. It is not Sympathy with a Viet Nam orphan, a wounded animal, a ravaged environment. Sympathy calls for us to consider ourselves as beings apart who can feel sorry for the problems of others, and that is where it is deficient. Its presumption that we stand alone, that we are self-sufficient, that our Selves must be preserved before all else: it is this basic outlook that has made the world the wretched place that it is today. Empathy, on the other hand, calls for involvement: you do not feel sorry, or glad, or pained because another is sorry or glad or in pain; you **feel** the others sorrow, happiness, pain because it is your sorrow, happiness, pain. You empathise when you see the world through the eyes and the emotions of others. You empathise when you say "How would I feel in that person's place?", "What would be my pain if I was that animal locked in a cage?", "What would be my feelings if I was that stretch of river filled with filth and pollution from a factory?"

Such empathy was a normal way of life in ancient India. Animals, plants, rivers, mountains, countries, nations, the very forces of nature, each had their guardian deity, each was personified: an excellent device to promote universal empathy. If you misuse the earth, the Earth Goddess will punish you, if you are unkind to an animal the guardian deity of the beast will strike you. But we have lost this talent for empathy and must, therefore, make an effort to rediscover it.

Do not tell us that you cannot put yourself in another's place: people do it all the time. A mother empathises with her child when she empathises with its home-sickness even though she knows that she, herself, would not feel such anguish in such circumstances. An animal lover empathises with a tiger when he sees it performing acrobatics in a circus. A writer empathises with a river when he writes movingly about its pollution. The greatest leaders of mankind, all down the ages, have not been the ones with a feeling of sympathy, but those who have had the gift of empathy.

And empathy is the ability to dissolve your own ego and expand it to embrace the Self of others. Only by losing your obsession with your limited self can you realise your empathised self which will, eventually, embrace the whole of creation.

In the last exercise you experienced the glimmerings of empathy. In this exercise we shall teach you how to deepen your awareness, using your Tantric partner as an instrument, as your Tantric partner will use you.

Do not attempt these exercises unless you have succeeded in the flame-merging exercise with your Tantric partner. If both of you have felt the strange elation of that discipline, and have progressed at an equal pace, you are now ready to take the next step.

These exercises call for strict continence: there must be no intercourse, no hurrying to an orgasmic goal. You must also stop all other, earlier, exercises mentioned in this book: if you wish to revise any of the earlier exercises, do so. Go back to them and repeat them in any of their variations, as often as you and your partner feel you should. Come back to this chapter only when you are certain that you have reached this level by mastering all that has gone before.

We recommend that you should start these exercises only when you and your Tantric partner can afford to take a three-day break from your normal avocations. It would be best if both of you leave your normal environment and go to a hill-station, a beach resort, a remote off-season hotel. You must be able to devote the entire three days to yourselves without risk of distraction. If you do so, if you cut yourselves off from the daily chores which govern your every-day lives, then we assure you that the benefits you will receive from adhering to these disciplines will more than compensate for your enforced holiday. You will return to your work refreshed, renewed, invigorated.

We shall spread the exercises over the three days and shall tell you our proposals for each day. The proposals are, in turn, in two parts: one for the morning and the other for the evening. We suggest that you read the proposals together, sitting or lying close to each other but that both of you should make a special effort to avoid any heightened sexual stimulation. We repeat that there should be no sexual intercourse between you until the evening of the third day: you will come very near it because some of the exercises are provocative, but you must not give way to your yearnings. Remember that Tantra teaches you how to prolong the act of love and if you give into yourselves now you will have thrown away all that has gone before. Read our proposals every morning before you go out... you could do it when you are both lying in bed, or after breakfast... and in the evening either before or after dinner. The proposals will suggest what you should do together till the next session of reading: some will be easy to follow, most will be difficult, but please follow them to the letter. Believe us... and we are speaking from experience... they can be adhered to, and if you adhere to them you will experience a depth to your loving that you have never experienced before. You will also have taken a great step forward in your Tantric journey.

THE FIRST DAY

Do you remember how you first met? And what you talked about? How long has it been since you really spoke to each other? Do you remember what it felt like when you first discovered that you had common interests, and how you probed and questioned and wondered? Human beings are very trusting when they're young, and then they find that if they are too trusting they get hurt and so they draw into themselves. And every time someone hurts them they become less trusting, less open, more drawn into themselves.

And then they find someone whom they can trust again. They don't want to believe it. They are careful. They want to know if they can really trust that person, or if that person will let them down. They want to be trusting, they want to open their hearts, they want to re-discover that sense of wonder they lost as a child, but they don't want to be hurt.

You two are together now because you trust each other. But you don't trust each other completely. There is always that Seventh Veil that you hold between your real selves and everyone else in the world, because the Seventh Veil is the last defence you have between the real you and those who might hurt you. Some people... most people... never let down the Seventh Veil, they never really reveal what they feel or think. You two are very near dropping the Seventh Veil but it is the most difficult one to remove because when you remove it you will have nothing left to hide. You will stand as naked before each other as you have never been before.

Today we will help the two of you to see through each other's Seventh Veils. A brief glimpse is enough to re-establish the faith that you have lost. But it takes time and, because you have given yourselves time, you will succeed.

Go for a walk this morning. When did you last go for a walk with no other purpose but to get to know each other? A month ago? A year? Two years? Or have you forgotten?

It doesn't matter. The past does not matter unless you want to hide it: and if either of you want to hide the past from the other it is not likely that you would have come here, together.

Go for a walk, hold hands if you want to, and talk. Talk of anything and everything. Talk of your fears, your loves, your hates. Complement each other. Speak of anything but one: do not, today, say anything which might hurt your partner. If you speak of a past love affair, remember to add that it is over and done with; if you find fault with something your partner has done, and must speak of it, always add that the good far outweighs the bad.

But there is no need to even mention such painful things. If you had met for the first time, if you were attracted to each other, you would not speak of things that would hurt. Imagine that you have met for the first time. You are both keen to show how much you care, what a nice person you are to be with. Lovers are always on their best behaviour because they are sensitive of each others moods, feelings, needs. They have empathy for each other. Pretend that you are not lovers as yet, but that you hope to become lovers if things work out, and both of you want things to work out.

Court each other. Courting is an old-fashioned word but it describes the process of mutual attraction, and all that follows, as no other word does. It means politeness, and gallantry, and charm, and consideration. Be polite and gallant and charming and considerate to each other today.

Do not be aggressively male. The aggressive male is rude, crude, unpolished. Do not be heavily female. The heavy female is dumb, subservient, docile. Both these are excessive qualities and have their place in the scheme of things, but their place is not here, not today.

Give yourselves a chance to get to know each other as human beings.

Remember, always, when you walk out today, that you are trying to court each other and find the love you have been searching for. Become young teen-agers again. You have just discovered the delight of meeting people of the other sex. Young teen-agers court each other instinctively. Let your instincts make you do the mad, wild, crazy things: offering a flower, laughing at cloud shapes, building castles in the air. Let your hair down, forget the world, be alive only to each other, and walk and talk, talk, talk.

But do not kiss, do not fondle each other, do not make love. Hold all that back in spite of your greatest urgings. Touch the light surface of your desires and live off the froth of them.

Today you are a young teen-ager: hesitant, uncertain, and keen to make an impression on the girl who has agreed to go for a walk with you, or the boy who has asked you to walk with him alone, on this wonderful spring-feeling day. And it doesn't matter if it's Spring, Summer, Monsoon, Autumn or Winter.

It is always Spring when two young people go for a walk alone because the whole world sings for people who are certain that they will find love.

And now go out together, and find each other, and love.

The Evening of THE FIRST DAY

What happened today? Did you like it? Did you discover things that you had forgotten? Did you feel warmer, happier, more alive than you have felt for a long time? You must have if you have relaxed in each other's company and searched for those laughing days of your teens.

Now that you are alone and the evening has come, talk about the things you did. Talk softly, gently, laughingly. If you find a great need to make love, talk about it. Describe what you feel, but do not make love. Kiss if you must, but do not caress, do not undress in each other's presence, do not excite each other by sight, or touch, only by words. Express the tension that is in you. Describe what you would like to do to each other, but do not do it. Hold back yourselves. You have a long time ahead of you to make love in all the ways that you can think of and many that you have never even imagined before. Think of them, talk about them, describe them, but there must be no sexual act tonight.

Calm yourselves down tonight and, if you can do it without making love, sleep in each others arms. Remember that you must learn self-control and that the sooner you learn it the better. Tomorrow you will touch. Day-after-tomorrow you can make love. Hold back yourselves and you will find an ecstasy, 48 hours from now, that you never knew existed. And if you can't sleep because you want each other so badly, talk it out. With the force of the yearning in you, both of you will come close to piercing the Seventh Veil for the first time in your lives.

THE SECOND DAY

What happened last night, or this morning? Did you succumb? Did you make love? We hope you didn't because if you did you will have decreased the valuable force of sexual pressure that you will need today. But if you have made love try and go through today's exercises with greater care than you could muster yesterday.

If you have not made love, if you are still full of the sexual pressure, of self-control, then you have gained a great victory: very few people in your position could have restricted themselves. But then there are very few Tantrists and you are well on the path to becoming one.

But regardless of whether you did or did not make love yesterday, the next two days....and that includes the day before you...will really be tough and if you get through them without succumbing to your urges you will be ready for the last step that we can show you in this book, and the bliss that that step will bring.

This is what you must do today.

Close the doors and windows of your room. Bathe separately using the yoga hygiene techniques we have described. And then strip and sit facing each other, your eyes open.

Now, very gently, very delicately, begin to stroke each other. The touches must be light and completely unsexual. The woman must not be touched on the breasts or the genital organs regardless of how erect her nipples might get, or how much she might moisten. The man must not be touched on his penis or his testicles regardless of the rigidity of his erection.

Stroke as if you were touching a baby, or a flower. Your touch must never be heavy, never erotic. Do not speak when you touch each other for if you speak you might upset the delicate balance of self-control that is so necessary now. Say nothing, make no overtly sexual gestures, but touch and stroke and stroke and touch till you feel yourself bursting with the strength of your desires.

You might both begin to sweat. The woman might cry, the man might tremble. Stop only if it becomes unbearable and you cannot stroke because of the sweat, or the crying, or the trembling.

If you do not sweat, or cry, or tremble, stop stroking after half an hour. If you are doing it correctly, giving it all your attention, you will not be able to take more than half an hour of it knowing that you cannot end it in the relief of an orgasm.

Stretch out on your backs, then, side by side, holding hands if necessary, and be very still, breathing deeply. If the pressure of blood in your genitals is excessive and is not relieved by your lying down for ten minutes, do a shoulder-stand with your chin locked firmly in your necks. Women often find difficulty in doing a shoulder stand because of the additional weight on their hips. Use a chair for support. A shoulder stand causes the blood to be dispersed from the genital region and relieves the pain of prolonged engorgement. Rest again after the shoulder stand and then bathe, separately, in **warm** water. We emphasise **warm** water. If you cannot get warm water, try and sleep and do not bathe until you are completely relaxed.

And then, when you have bathed and rested, commence stroking again. This time it will not be so difficult to continue because your body has grown used to the pace of the stroking. Do it for about ten or fifteen minutes the second time.

Relax again and bathe. You are likely to feel very hungry. Eat a light snack and then go for a leisurely walk and take it easy. You have been through a very rugged discipline and you might not want to talk. You might want only to walk, and hold hands, and think. Or then, again, you might want to talk and share your experiences, tell each other what you felt while you were being stroked. You might even want to give up the entire exercise as a waste of time and far too strenuous for you. Don't be disappointed if you feel this way: most people do. We are not used to restraining ourselves in sex when we are alone with a willing partner, and the more the pressure you have worked up during your stroking the more power you have generated to use, and the more difficult it is to refrain from relieving the tension. If the thought is of any reassurance, our experience has led us to believe that the people who are nearest to success are the ones who most want to give in. They have worked up the greatest sexual pressure and so they find it most difficult to restrain themselves. But remember that the athlete who pushes himself to the limits of his normal endurance, and then pushes himself over that limit, is the one who will become a star. The others give up.

We intend to push you beyond the limits of your normal sexual endurance.

So walk and talk and relax: tonight you will both face the trial again.

The Evening of the SECOND DAY

We hope you have not eaten heavily, but if you have, relax, preferably in the open air, for at least two hours after your meal. Then bathe, strip and sit opposite each other.

Now, when you begin stroking, we want you to make a mental adjustment.

When you stroke your partner feel the touch on your partner's body as if your partner were touching you. When you touch your partner on the shoulder feel your touch on your shoulder; when you touch your partner on the cheek, feel the touch on your cheek. While you are doing this your partner will be touching you. Deaden yourself to that touch. The touch you feel must be your own, not your partner's. Similarly your partner must not feel your touch.

We shall repeat that.

You, the man, are touching the woman. When you touch her on her throat, imagine that you are touching your own throat. She might be touching you on your shoulder at this time: do not concentrate on her touch ou your shoulder.

You, the woman, are touching the man. When you touch him on the shoulder imagine that you are touching your own shoulder. He might be touching you on your throat at this time: do not concentrate on his touch on your throat.

It is not as difficult to do as it appears in print. After fifteen minutes of practice both of you should be able to do it. In fact when you stretch out your hand to touch her throat, the skin on your throat will tingle in anticipation of your touch; and when you reach for his shoulder, the skin on your shoulder will tingle in anticipation of your touch.

Keep this up for not less than half an hour and not more than an hour.

If you have made the correct mental adjustment you will find that the erotic stimulation of the touching is of a different quality from the one you experienced yesterday. It is intense but not gross. It is more like an inner glow rather than a driving force. It makes you feel light and unreal. You feel this way because you are trying, virtually, to shift your Centre of Consciousness to your partner. You and your partner are exchanging something close to personalities.

This exercise will give you a degree of empathy with your partner that is almost telepathic and it is, therefore, an exercise that you will have to continue throughout your Tantric life.

But, this first day, do not indulge in any sexual touches. The man may touch the fullness and curve of the woman's breasts: not her nipples, and he must not clutch or squeeze her breasts. The woman must not, under any circumstances, even stroke the man's penis.

And again, no sexual intercourse. If the tension gets too strong, relax, do the shoulder stand, bathe, rest.

Most couples do not find it too difficult to fall asleep after this exercise.

THE THIRD DAY

After a light breakfast, strip, and continue your empathic stroking, but now you may.... very, very lightly ...stroke the nipples, the vulva, and the penis. The strokes must be light and, again, they must be anticipated on your own body. When the woman strokes the man's penis she must feel the strokes on her vulva; similarly when the man strokes the woman's vulva he must feel the strokes on his penis.

Again, prolong your stroking for an hour, then relax and breathe deeply for five minutes.

And then the man must lie on his back and the woman must sit straddling his body, facing him and.... very slowly, very gently.... insert his penis into herself.

After which there must be no movements. The woman should stretch out and lie on the man, with his penis inserted in her, but both must be physically very still.

Keep lying till the man's erection has subsided. There must be no orgasm, only stillness and a deep shared empathy and contentment.

Both you and your partner must ensure that the man is in control of himself when the woman receives his erect penis into her. The man should permit this only when he is certain that the handling and insertion of his penis will not send him into an orgasmic spasm. The woman must ensure that she can control her movements and will not, herself, go into orgasm once she feels the fullness of her partner's penis entering her.

If you can prolong the sexual connection, without orgasm, and if both of you can fall asleep with your bodies locked in sex, you will awake unusually refreshed, invigorated and with a strange empathic bond. But even if you cannot fall asleep, if you can remain locked together till the man's erection subsides, you will still feel richly rewarded.

After this, walk again and do as you will, but no sexual intercourse.

The evening of THE THIRD DAY

Go through the entire empathic stroking exercise for

an hour at least. Be very strict about this. Your stroking must be empathic, and it must be prolonged for an
hour at the very least.

And then, when you have virtually exchanged personalities and are feeling lit up with shared sexual pressure, give way to your sexual urges.

For the first time in three days have sexual intercourse
with your Tantric partner.

It is likely that you will have intercourse more than
once.

And, if you have followed our advice carefully for
these three days, it is certain that you will never have
experienced a more ecstatic orgasm.

You are now ready for the last exercise: the strange
post-orgasmic trance called FLOATING.

Chapter Eleven

Floating

As we have mentioned earlier, the symbol of Tantra is the phallus: the erect penis, not the flaccid, post-orgasmic, organ. Many reasons have been given for this symbolism but it is certainly not the most obvious one that strikes the western-oriented mind: Tantra is not, basically, a male-biased discipline. To the contrary. The Shakti, the Great Mother, is the active principle of Tantra. It is she who dances, she who creates this world of illusions, she who is worshipped by the Primal Male Himself. "Why then," you may ask, "is the phallus the symbol? Surely for a female deity the vulva would be more appropriate?" In actual fact, the complete symbol of Tantra is the Phallus in the receptive Vagina: the Lingam in the Yoni. In other words, the principal sacrament of Tantra is sexual intercourse, **before orgasm.** And the longer this state can be maintained, the greater will be the benefit you and your partner can derive from Tantra.

We shall not, however, speak about the methods of delaying orgasm in this chapter. Such prolongation, in our opinion, is merely a matter of practice and technique, and a considerable degree of 'holding power' will have been obtained from the exercises in the last chapter. If you can control the mind and the sensations it will not be very difficult to delay orgasm. The positions of intercourse, given in the next chapter, can merely enhance an already acquired skill, they cannot teach the skill itself. In this chapter, therefore, we shall describe the methods of reaching the special state of Tantric bliss that prolonged intercourse can offer. We shall also describe the technique you should use to apply this bliss towards the solution of your mundane problems.

Tantric Sex must be:
    Prolonged
    Unhurried
    Effortless.

The words are not synonymous even though their edges
might appear to overlap.

Tantric Sex must be Prolonged

Tantric Sex starts from the instant that the two partners feel an attraction towards other: it does not
matter whether they are out in the street, or at work,
or even dreaming. As soon as the first spark of sexuality
is ignited, the act of Tantric Sex has begun. Thus you
will see that when both the partners are aware of the
Duality of Creation, and have directed their response to
that Duality towards each other, their sexual involvement with each other is an unending act. It is for this
reason that we say that Tantric Lovers are on a perpetual
honeymoon, living in an endless spring-fever. If you
appreciate this basic fact of Tantra you will appreciate
our reasoning when we say that Tantric Sex is, literally,
prolonged throughout the lives of the Tantric partners
and thus no specific act in this involvement is more important than any other. To start with, therefore, Tantra
removes the west's preoccupation with intercourse. The
total preoccupation of the two partners is so constant
and profound that intercourse is merely another incident
in the continuing act of love, and Tantric saints reveal
this constant preoccupation with ecstasy in all its forms.
We are indebted to Philip Rawson's TANTRA: THE
INDIAN CULT OF ECSTASY for the following description of what a Tantric saint looks like to an outsider.

> He is so happy as to seem crazy; his eyes roll, red-
> dened with wine. He sits on silk cushions surroun-
> ded by works of art, eating hot pork cooked with
> chillies. At his left side sits a girl skilled in the
> arts of love, with whom he drinks and repeatedly
> has ecstatic sexual intercourse; he continually makes
> music with his vina, and sings poems; all of which

he weaves together into rituals. Everything that such a man seems to be and do gives violent offence to the conventionally minded. And that in fact is part....but only part....of the point. For he himself has had to break any lingering attachment he may have had even to his own conventional attitudes. What he is doing fundamentally is rousing all the energies he can discover in his body, emotions and mind, and combining them into a vehicle which will carry him towards enlightenment: enlightenment being that state of knowledge, the truth about the origin of things and men, and their meaning, as clearly as experiencing the street. He uses every possible means, adapting every conceivable emotional stimulus and act to his purpose, on the assumption that things which you actually do repeatedly, and which have associated with them a powerful sensuous and emotive charge, change you far more effectively than anything else. And only if you combine together many kinds of doing is the change radical.

From this it is clear that the act of Tantric Sex is a constant preoccupation with all Tantrists because, according to Tantra, all creation has a sexual base and Tantrists make themselves aware of this great truth.

However, in spite of the constant sexuality of all Tantrists, it cannot be denied that sexual intercourse does have a significance all its own, as indeed anything capable of being distinguished from other things has a significance all its own. The special significance of intercourse is that it brings the partners into the closest physical contact and thus allows for the greatest degree of interpersonal stimulus. It is also the most condusive to orgasm. Thus, in Tantric terms, the greatest benefit can be derived from intercourse only if the inter-personal stimulus is as high as you and your partner can achieve.

We shall explain this statement.

In the second part of this book we had devoted considerable time to a description of the Tantric Room, Erotic Dress, Sexual Exercises etc. We have not, how-

ever, told you when all this is to be used. The reason
why we have not gone into the details of the use of the
'equipment' is that we expect you and your Tantric
partner to be imaginative and innovative. We do not
want to describe, in detail, how you should conduct your
love play, because it would be quite pointless for us to
do so. We presume that you are experienced lovers
and have, thus, become very familiar with each other's
erotic likes and dislikes. We, therefore, suggest that
you provide yourself with the 'equipment' so that when
you want to tap a particular erotic stimulus you do not
have to search around for the means to do it. What
we do insist on, however, is that your love-making is as
long as you can comfortably extend it. To take a case
in point, if the male Tantrist can sit through an hour-
long performance by a professional stripper, keeping
himself sexually tense all the time, his partner should
be able to keep him sexually amused for at least as
long. The chapter on Dress and the section on illumination for the Tantric Room suggests all the 'equipment'
needed to duplicate a stripper's stimulating performance.
Similarly, if the female Tantrist can keep a group of
beach-boys oogling at her for an hour, and get a sexual
thrill out of their admiration, she can do the same thing
in her sunken bath and in the Love Garden, with her
Tantric partner in place of the beach-boys.

Thus, if you and your partner have accepted our
suggestions....and, if necessary, those in the next
chapter.... you will have the means of prolonging
your acts of sexual foreplay and intercourse beyond the
normal.

Tantric Sex Must be Unhurried

A thing can be both Prolonged and Hurried. The
word 'hurry', in this context, refers to the western-
oriented need to complete a job as quickly as possible.
Thus it might be possible for a Tantric pair to plan a
comprehensive programme of foreplay and positions of
intercourse which could take them well over two hours
to go through. Nevertheless, each specific act in the

sequence could be hurried through in keeping with the western-oriented version of efficiency.

Please always remember, in everything you do, that it is the ultimate goal that matters; all your conduct must be directed towards the achievement of that goal.

The ultimate goal of Tantra is Supreme Ecstasy and Knowledge. This is a goal which cannot be fitted into a time-framework because it is beyond time. You must, therefore, be as free of temporal limitations as you can when you are engaged in a search for this goal.

We do appreciate, of course, that as people who have to live in a time-constrained society, it is not possible to be entirely free of the dictates of the clock, but within its limitations you must ensure the greatest possible freedom from time schedules. This sounds contradictory, but it is not, as we shall show you.

You must, necessarily, budget the time you can spend on Tantric Sex. Let us say that you have decided to spend two hours together in the Tantric Room. You also have a rough idea of what you want to do: both you and your partner might have been stimulated by an erotic book, a graphic picture, an idea sown by friend's conversation. Any one, or all of these, have prompted you to plan certain erotically — appealing acts for your Tantric period. This is an excellent start to your Tantric session and it proves that you are constantly alert to the sexual possibilities of the world around you. We also agree that it is fun to plan what you and your partner intend to do: it certainly raises the sexual pressure.

All that we ask you to do is to be flexible about the routine you have planned for yourselves. Do not, for instance, say that you have two hours before you and therefore you intend to spend twenty minutes in erotic dressing up, fifty minutes in stroking, twenty minutes in other foreplay and thirty minutes in intercourse. This schedule may sound absurd to most of us but we assure you that it has been drawn directly from the experience from one of our American friends. They claimed that they had practiced all that we had recommended to them but they were not making any headway at all. We found this so contrary to our experience that we questioned them about what they did. The male Tantrist... or Tantrist-to-be.... pulled out a diary and started reading out their sex routines over the previous 45 days, assuring us that they had adhered to the schedules to the minute!

Well, of course, this might be all very well in a high-pressure American College when trying to graduate **summa cum laude,** but you cannot work-study yourself into effective Tantra!

What we are trying to say is that within your two hours you should take as much time in any one act as your fancy dictates. You and your partner must realise that you are entirely free to devote as much, or as little, time to fantasy, stroking, varied positions, or slow, deliberate, intercourse as the moment inspires. Explore all the sexual byways, backwaters and shaded paths that you and your partner would not, otherwise, have had time for. You do not have to have intercourse, an orgasm is not necessary. Nothing is essential except your own sexual tension and joy in what you and your partner are doing. And the more unhurried both of you are the longer you can sustain it and the more sexual power you will generate.

Tantric Sex Must be Effortless

Tantra is also known as Tantric Yoga; and all yoga to be effective must be effortless. Trained Hatha Yoga instructors insist that their pupils learn the asanas with their eyes wide open. The eyes are the first to show signs of tiredness and yoga, unlike all other systems of physical exercise, insists that you should feel no strain whilst doing it. What is required is the will and determination: but there must be absolutely no physical strain.

With Tantra, too, only your will and your determination must be strained, not your body. In fact, if you strain your body you build up an accumulation of the by-products of fatigue and your physical tenacity decreases. For instance, a man who wants to retain his orgasm must not retain his breath and tighten his buttocks: if he does so he will snap himself into the orgasmic spasm sooner than he expected. But if he relaxes, breathes deeply, and loosens his buttock muscles, he re-establishes control over his orgasmic response.

When you are involved in Tantric Sex do every movement as gracefully, rhythmically and effortlessly as possible. Grace, rhythm and effortlessness conserve energy and you must conserve all the energy you can. Sex, in Tantra, is the dance of life and it must be indulged in as gracefully as if you were dancing.

Enjoy the flow of movement, the smooth response of your body to your partner's and that of your partner's body to yours. This is where your co-ordinated exercises become very valuable, and the empathy that exists between you and your partner plays a very important part in such co-ordination. Flow from one action to the next, from one movement to the next, from one desire to the next so that there is no consciousness of where one ends and the other begins but only that there is an unbroken continuity of love and understanding.

When you achieve this effortlessness you will find that you have lost all consciousness of passing time because time, the way we understand it, is a sequence of events, one following the other. Thus when you are bored and remove your attention from the sequence of events immediately around you, time seems to slow; similarly, when you are very interested in something and eagerly look forward to a continuation of the pleasing activity, time seems to speed up because your anticipation blurs your consciousness of the individual events in the sequence.

Thus, it is clear, that intercourse follows as a natural sequence in the flow of events that is Tantric Sex. There should be no need for a conscious decision of the partners to have intercourse at any point during their sexual involvement with each other, except in the special circumstances dealt with in the next chapter. Intercourse should be as natural as a spark bursting into flame, clouds bringing rain, or the ebb and flow of the tides. Please do not consider these figures of speech as entirely symbolic: there is little in Tantra that is entirely symbolic. As

Tantra is a system of universal awareness and expansion of the consciousness, fire and rain and tides are very much a part of the experience of the Tantrist and you will soon realise that you, yourself, will have to describe your experiences in similar terms.

When can a Tantrist expect these experiences? There is, naturally, no certain answer to that question: it depends on the stimulus given, the response of the partners, the degree of consciousness expansion reached by the two Tantrists. But, if experience is any guide, there is one threshold that must be crossed before the mind begins to expand. For want of a better word we refer to this doorway as the experience of Floating.

FLOATING

The experience of Floating is most intense, but briefest, immediately after orgasm and many sensitive people experience it without knowing what it is: a glowing, trance-like ecstasy. It can, however, occur at any time after the intromission of the penis in the vagina. Please note that we have used the word 'intromission' and not 'intercourse'. 'Intercourse' conveys the impression of physical activity and movement, whereas 'Intromission' refers merely to the act of the insertion of the lingam in the receptive yoni: the primal symbol of Tantra. Some Tantrists claim that intromission is not necessary for the experience of Floating and there is every likelihood that advanced Tantrists are so immersed in the ecstasy of creation that they are in a perpetual state of sexual ecstasy verging on orgasm. When one reaches that state then the physical act of sex becomes redundant. But as far as the average reader of this book is concerned it would be wise to take it as axiomatic that the experience of Floating can only come about after prolonged Tantric Sex followed by the insertion of the male sexual organ into the female.

At this stage you should have reached a degree of ego-dissolution where the individual personality is merged in the personality of the partner or, at the very least, where the two have reached a level of sexual ecstasy verging on semi-consciousness. It is very much like the 'little death' following orgasm but this is a prolonged state: the normal orgasmic peak has been extended to a plateau of the same level of ecstasy.

If you and your partner have reached this, lie back with your eyes closed, your sexual organs still connected, and let your muscles go limp. It is advisable to keep your lower limbs inter-locked to maintain the physical intimacy even when you are relaxing for, as we have said, the physical connection seems to be very necessary for the experience of Floating.

Shortly after you close your eyes and relax your muscles, drifting with the ecstasy your partner and you are experiencing....for this is a time of great empathy with your partner....you will be buoyed with a strange feeling of detatchment from the body. Some have described this sensation as that of rising, others as that of falling, but it is in fact a feeling of weightlessness similar to the one experienced by astronauts in gravity-free space. Those who have prior knowledge of this experience....it also occurs to some imaginative people just before they fall asleep sometimes....will not resist it. Most, however, will tend to panic and will find themselves back to normal. If this happens, the weightless feeling is unlikely to occur in the same sexual encounter. If, however, the feeling is not resisted and you give yourself to it without anxiety, the rising or falling sensation will stop after a while; in other words, the initial sensation of motion will cease and be replaced by a gentle, suspended, feeling. This is extremely pleasant and relaxing and has been described by various Tantrists as: "Drifting on a down-soft cloud"; "Gliding on an up-draft"; "Zephyr-blown like cotton-wool"; "Floating on an ethereal sea". Our personal choice, and one which most closely describes our experience, is Floating.

Floating can be sustained almost indefinitely, provided you do not let your mind be invaded by anxiety or tension, or deliberately try to grasp the sensation. This last is most important: do not try to analyse the experience. Do not say to yourself "What am I experiencing?"

or, "How can I possibly be experiencing this?", or "Why am I experiencing this?".... What? When? Who? Where? and Why? should be totally excluded from your mind during the Floating experience. This will, possibly, be your first encounter with a vividly intuitive experience and any introduction of logical probing will destroy its fabric. There is no logic in intuition, and there is no intuition in logic, as far as you are concerned. Dr. Albert Einstein's logic might have been raised to the level of intuition, and St. John the Evangelist's intuition might have deepened to the level of logic, but for most of us the worlds of intuition and logic are independent and distinct and the disciplines of one must not be allowed to intrude into the disciplines of the other.

Drift, accept it, float in buoyed-up bliss and you will encounter a number of other-worldly Tantric experiences.

JOURNEY THROUGH THE MIND

You are now journeying through your mind into regions that you have never, consciously, visited before. Do not brush them aside as 'mere imagination' unless you can explain what imagination is: and if you **can,** then you have made a breakthrough in mental research, from the western point of view.

We shall now recount a generalized version of the experience of a number of Tantrists. Your individual experience is likely to vary in many details though, we believe, the pattern will be similar in most respects. If the experience is frightening, depressing, or excessively exciting, we advise you to desist from further journeys and seek competent Tantric help. These journeys are the original versions of psychedelic trips and though.... unlike the drug induced visions.... they are through the 'front-door' of perception, careless exposure to them might inflict damage to immature wills and minds. Unlike the drug induced experience, these journeys have a cumulative effect: there is ample time for the cautious voyager to withdraw if the going gets too rough.

Colour: glows of primary colours followed by slabs

and blocks of glowing translucence floating in grey space and occupying most of your field of vision. At first the shapes of the modules appear to be defined like floating sections of luminous ice but as you look at them drifting before you, the edges lose their distinction as if they were curling, like smoke, into themselves to form into stars and blobs and asterisks which change their perspective and colour relevant to you as if they had been photographed by variously angled cameras and the images projected to you in disconnected succession. This is the most pleasing and pyrotechnic of the displays, but they are merely introductions, curtain-raisers, as it were, for the main images.

The first group of main images come now and they generally take the form of grotesque creatures, incredible amalgams of man-beast-plant-mineral. They are not necessarily frightening although they appear to gibber and grin: your physical connection with your Tantric partner always provides an under-base of assurance when these entities appear. We have reason to believe that these creatures have real existence but we cannot say if, in reality, they are as our mind sees them. Indeed, if they are immaterial personalities then their 'images' are fabricated by our minds because we are used to viewing reality in such terms. We also feel that only an experienced Tantrist can risk encountering them alone for, without the reassurance of physical contact with a fellow Tantrist, most of us might well become mentally scarred, acting as if we were 'possessed' by these entities. This is probably what happens during a bad psychedelic trip. This much we do assure you: though we have heard of such cases, we have not, personally, come across a single instance of a coupled Tantric pair having a bad Tantric trip; they have always felt in complete control of the images perceived during a Tantric journey.

In passing we would also like to mention that the entities that Tantrists see are neither essentially good nor essentially evil. They appear to be elemental powers of nature and can be controlled by the use of suitable sound patterns and the strength of will acquired through prolonged austerities. These are the 'genies' of the Arabian Nights, the 'familiars' of western witches, and the taunting demons of ascetics of all religions. When held in subservience to a human will they account for the 'miracles' performed by many of the famous mystics and holy men. We shall not, however, go into the lore of these spirits because they are a study....and a dangerous study.... in themselves.

The visions of the disembodied entities give way to the most beautiful landscapes: rolling golden fields under a bright emerald sun; vistas of crystal ice-floes bathed in an all-pervasive blue light; stately ebony-trunked forests their moss-green foliage aflame with blossoms of saffron, mauve, strawberry, lilac and dusty silver; cloud-piercing mountains, island-dotted seas, under-water sea-scapes florescing in incredible hues. And always you seem to be floating high above the landscape, sometimes slowly, sometimes at great speed. At first you will not be able to control the change of scene, but in time you will become aware....it is not a logical learning process but an intuitive awareness process....of the effortless push that you can give to your floating Self to skim over these other-worldly scenes.

At this stage most lower-level seekers fall asleep. We shall, however, describe the next stages of the journey which, we hope, you will eventually advance to.

The landscapes appear to be actual scenes drawn from the space-time spanning awareness of mankind's racial Overmind and, with practice, it is at this stage that Tantrists can see across distances and pierce the veil of the past and the future.

If you do not deliberately pause here, however, the landscape stage gives way to bright geometrical patterns and the seeker becomes aware of the related sound. In actual fact both the images and the sound are vibrations interpreted by your sense-accustomed mind as visions and notes, the notes being the more subtle of the vibrations. Though they have both been present throughout your mental journey, it takes some time for your mind to become conscious of the sound. In the higher vibratory stages, however, the definition of the sound-vibrations increases and that of the image-vibrations decreases. It is for this reason that the images now assume the closest approximations to pure vibrations: perfect geometric forms, holding static for moments and the changing to even purer forms with the hypnotic fascination of a kaleidoscope. The images appear to be so fine as to seem almost colourless against the increasingly bright background towards which they are moving. A peculiarity of these images is that, in spite of the fact that they change rapidly, their focal point never shifts. It almost seems as if you are moving, with increasing speed, down a clear tunnel whose walls are formed by the geometric shapes which appear, grow, fill your vision, and vanish behind as you sweep past deeper and deeper towards the brightening centre.

Various explanations have been given for this imagery but the most reasonable one appears to be that you are now soaring through time towards an encounter with your timeless Self, locked in eternal ecstasy with its Shakti, and these geometric forms are the nascent objects which are spewed out by the mouth of time on their way to form the reality of the present and the past.

At this stage the sound becomes an all-pervasive thing almost more real than the images. It has been variously described as the humming of a huge conch shell, the giant hum produced by a stroked prayer bell, and the chant of OM greatly magnified. Now, too, the light bathes you with an indescribable ecstasy both drawing you in and exploding you outwards as if inwards and outwards were the same thing and only by embracing all creation in bliss can you find the ecstasy that lies pin-pointed at the centre of the light, beckoning you on and on and on......

That is as much as we can describe without having to rely wholly on others' experiences. In all likelihood it will be a very long time before you can cross the level of the landscapes: after that you will have to seek guidance from your personal guru. We would, however, like to acquaint you with one more discipline before we leave you: it is a simple discipline which taps the problem-solving powers of Tantra.

PROBLEMS AND TANTRA

If you have a problem which you wish Tantra to solve, first study it in detail. Fill your mind with all the information, relevant to the problem, that you can lay your hands on. This gives direction to your mind. Next, roughly formulate the various courses of action open to you and the possible consequences of each course of action. We realise that you will not be able to study all the facts concerning the problem, or examine all the possibilities, or assess all the consequences, but the mind must be convinced that you have gone as far as you logically can. You must bring your mind to the limit of logic and to the border of intuition.

Having done that, hand your problem over to your sub-conscious in an actual mental act of handing over: picture yourself handing your problem to a shadowy presence standing against the dark, spark-lit, depths of your hidden mind.

And then give your attention to Tantric Sex.

When you reach the stage of Floating over the landscapes of the Otherworld, do not force the pace even if you know how to, but fall asleep in the course of the ecstasy of your Floating journey.

The answer to your problem will come to you, unbidden, within the next 48 hours.

LIVING ECSTASY

Finally, and quite apart from the imagery, the prolonged sex of Tantra gives you and your partner orgasms that are indescribable in their intensity. It also brings you and your partner so close to each other that both of you will find yourselves wanting to embrace total strangers, becoming sensually receptive to an unbelievable degree, and developing an empathy that makes you one with the whole of burgeoning, fecunding, striving creation around you.

Tantra gives an unending awareness of the living ecstasy that is Creation.

Part IV

SEXUAL POSITIONS

Chapter Twelve

Prolonged Sex

One of the first victims of western man's unseemly haste is his sex life. Efficiency is measured by the speed with which a person completes an act effectively, and an effective act of sex is an act which results in orgasm....or so the west would have us believe. In other words, the quicker the orgasm the more effective the intercourse. This strange perversion of values has resulted in us glorifying the male who can copulate with the greatest number of females and the female who is most willing to forego the delightful preliminaries of civilized sex. Nowadays, novelists make heroines of women who seem to be eternally ready for copulation and we recall reading a book in which the female protagonist, whilst returning from the coal cellar, encountered one of her husband's friends. The impatient friend manoeuvered the woman against a wall, unzipped her jeans, copulated with her, zipped her up, and then they both returned to the husband before he had finished his tea. Apart from his courage in facing the hazards of standing-face-to-face-coal-laden-intercourse, the friend must have suffered from a near-impotent attack of premature ejaculation: but obviously we were expected to admire the entire performance!

It is because **ejaculatio praecox** is virtually endemic to all westernized males, that this chapter needs to be written. And if any of our readers wishes to challenge our statement we would like them to refer to sex statistics on the subject as revealed by Kinsey and others orgasm, among western males, occurs ten seconds to two minutes after insertion. This is the norm and this is pathetic. If you and your partner follow the simple instructions we shall give you in this chapter we expect the male to be able to retain his orgasm for at least thirty minutes after insertion. With practice it should not be difficult to double, and even triple, this duration. We shall, of necessity, have to address this chapter to the male Tantrist because it is with him that the cure to this deplorable situation lies.

And we expect even the most experienced lovers to adhere to these rules. If the man cannot retain his erection for at least half an hour after insertion, both Tantric partners must go through this disciplined regimen: there is no other way to cure ejaculatio praecox, permanently.

Men, nowadays, embark on sex with the wrong ideas. We firmly believe that every act of Tantric Sex must be a seduction, sometimes by the man at other times by the woman. Men and women, however, have conflicting desires on this: one part of them tells them that postponement of intercourse will bring considerable sensuous rewards, but their engorged sexual organs urge them to relieve the sexual pressure as soon as possible. Tantra, wisely, prescribes a period of social intercourse before the sexual intercourse begins. Tantrists go through the gracious ritual of eating, drinking, and conversing before they take the final sacrament of sex. Tantric couples, in the privacy of their homes, cannot do better than to follow this routine. If the male is likely to ejaculate prematurely....a mere ten-minute westernized man.....the Tantric partners should court one another over light snacks and good alcohol. A mellow wine is the ideal drink, but in its absence any other drink will do. But please take it in moderation: moderate drinking loosens the inhibitions but dulls the orgasmic reflex **slightly**, which is exactly what is required. Too much drinking is likely to make the man temporarily impotent; he might not be able to get an erection at all!

The ancient Hindu art of kissing seems to have fallen into considerable disuse of late. Couples plunge headlong into the passionate, tonguing, kiss as if the probing tongues were emulating the probing penis. And, indeed, the similarity between the two acts is no coincidence, but there are many variations to the kiss....Kama Sutra lists 19 basic types.....and we recommend a kiss-

ing session as a delightful way of passing an hour or
two. It will also teach both partners the delights of
deferring orgasm and exploring other avenues of sensual
expression. We would like to make it clear that kissing
is a very natural form of erotic stimulus because the
lips and the tongue have a number of delicate nerves
that reflexively grab inserted objects when they come
in contact with them. It is this reflex that causes an
infant to suckle on its mother's breast and, later, suck
its thumb. But the nerves do not vanish when the
infant grows to manhood and, thus, the response of
the lips and tongue lasts throughout life. This need
for special stimulation of these mouth surfaces is satisfied by kissing; those who do not give themselves the
pleasure of such acts are frustrating themselves for no
purpose. There is, however, one danger to excessive
kissing: the body might get over-stimulated and want
to hurry to intercourse. It is, therefore, advisable for
the partners, if they find themselves in this state, to
'come up for air'. This is literally true: such love play
uses more energy than fairly vigorous exercise and unless
the partners stop and take a number of deep breaths,
occasionally, their bodies are likely to become sluggish
with fatigue-produced poisons which will tend to tense
the muscles and abort attempts at orgasmic control.
Well timed pauses for deep breathing are one of the
great secrets of prolonged intercourse.

You might have noticed that we have said nothing,
as yet, about either the male touching the female's
breasts, or of the female stroking the male's penis. This
is a deliberate omission on our part: we do not want
you to do either act at this stage. In fact we advise
the man to arch his body away from that of his partner's
so that his erect penis does not come into contact with
her.

When the partners have grown tired of mouth-to-mouth
kissing, the male should, very gradually, transfer his kisses
to his partner's neck and, slowly, work his mouth down
to her breasts. He should not touch the breasts as yet.
He should kiss the beginning of the valley between them,
the fullness of them above, below, around. Occasionally

he should move his lips over the nipples and breathe warmly on them, and then proceed to kiss the other parts of the breasts without touching the nipples with his lips. If these kisses are administered lightly, gently, lovingly, the nipples will begin to rise and harden in anticipation, and woman will move to make them touch her partner's lips. The man should not kiss these erect yearning peaks till both partners can resist it no longer; and then the male should breathe on them warmly again before licking them gently with his tongue. Only after he has licked both nipples, and thus prepared them for his lips, should he allow his lips to settle warmly and firmly around each of them in turn, sucking briefly.

Now the male should begin to stroke the female. The stroking should be soothing, as if trying to cool her, which is, indeed, what should be achieved. The object of this stroking is to give a slight pause to the erotic stimulus and thus allow both bodies to get used to this level of sexual pressure. The male should stroke the female's forehead and ears, eyes and cheeks, lips and throat, in gentle, outward, sweeping movements, taking in the head and neck in the last sweep before starting again. Every sweep of the hands should be followed by the lips gently kissing the areas touched. According to ancient eastern erotics, women's erogenous zones change with the curve of the menstrual cycle, and while the truth or otherwise of this belief has not been tested by science, it is a fact that women vary in their response to caresses: most preferring it on one part, one day, and on another part, the next. By lightly stroking his Tantric partner, and following it by gentle kisses, the male will be able to learn where the response of his partner is greatest and he should, naturally, increase his attention to those areas.

Here we would like to divert for a moment and recommend to you the benefit of expressing yourselves in uninhibited sounds during the course of your love play. It is a historic fact that when a nation conquers another, the language of the conquered people falls in status and, in time, becomes the 'gutter language'. This is what happened to the old Anglo-Saxon words when they were supplanted by their Latinised equivalents. And although all this happened over 1000 years ago, the bias against Anglo-Saxon words still exists. 'Intercourse' is acceptable, 'fucking' is not; 'penis', 'testicles' and 'vulva' are acceptable, 'cock', 'balls' and 'cunt' are not. These four letter words are so taboo that their usage carries a definite erotic charge: there is a stimulus in using the expression "Fuck me!" that does not exist in its latinised equivalents. Kama Sutra advises the woman to use the primal sounds of pleasure with advantage. We advise that both partners should encourage each other to use the Anglo-Saxon words... if English is their language of love... during Tantric Sex because the emotive charge of the words gives them an expressive, and erotic, power that evoke their own response, quite apart from their pithily expressive impact. The woman, in particular, will find her built-in inhibitions considerably loosened whenever she uses these words to describe what she wants and how she feels during her Tantric Sex encounters.

It is now right to begin a more obvious caressing of the breasts. Remember that the function of the breast is to provide milk and thus it is best stimulated if the normal milking action of an infant is duplicated. By this time the nipples should be hard and erect and ready to receive the caress of the man's hand. The man should use both his hands to squeeze both breasts at the same time. The entire structure of the breasts should be squeezed and he should gradually draw his hands towards the nipples as if he were intent on drawing milk from them. The squeezing should be gentle at first, and then gradually increased in force with particular attention being paid to the nipples, which should be gently pinched between thumb and forefinger. Some women also like the nipple to be grasped between the bent first and second fingers... as if the man were smoking a cigarette ....and the tip of the captured nipple lightly scratched with the nail of the thumb. The breast squeezing motion can also be combined with sucking. The infant-feeding illusion is appreciated by most women at this stage and so the man should lie at right angles to the body of the woman, resting his head on her chest or abdomen, sucking and caressing her breasts with affection. We emphasise 'affection' because aggressive actions will destroy the tender mother-and-child illusion.

We would like to caution against the woman touching the man in any erotic way. While there can be no objection to her caressing his face, head or upper body, we strongly advise against her making any contact with his penis even if the rigidity of the organ demands attention and the man is aching for it. Remember that this entire chapter is devoted to teaching the couple how to prolong the sexual contact and assist the man to delay his, normally quick, orgasm. Any touch on the engorged penis at this stage is likely to set the orgasmic spasm into motion and all our efforts at control will have been lost.

The man can now extend his caresses to the woman's back, buttocks, stomach, thighs and legs. Again, these touches should be light and stroking: a soothing motion rather than a stimulating one, although there is little doubt that the strokes will give a stimulus of a delicately erotic nature. These strokings, coupled with a reduction of the breast caresses, should help the woman, and the man, to relax slightly and make the woman more ready for prolonged intercourse.

The man should now let his hands stroke the thighs of the woman lightly and then draw his fingers over her vulva and across her stomach. This should be done a number of times along with strokings on other parts of her body, including the breasts. After some time the man should allow his arm to fall between the woman's legs, if she has not already parted her legs in anticipation, and on the upward movement of his fingers should allow them to enter the genital lips. He should not, however, plunge his fingers into the vagina of the woman, at this stage. The man's fingers should search for the clitoris, specifically, the ball of his index finger should try and touch the tip of this tiny erectile organ. Care should be taken that the finger-nail should not come into contact with this sensitive feminine tissue for the ensuing pain might frighten, and disgust, the woman. Some women have a hooded clitoris and so the entire organ lies under a thin sheath of tissue, and only the head is accessible to direct touch. The clitoris can be released by a simple surgical operation but there are certain erotic advantages to having such an organ: at the height of sexual activity the man need not be concerned with hurting the sensitive clitoris, and the active thrusting appreciated by the vagina will also be conveyed to the sheathed clitoris without any danger of it being crushed or hurt.

The handling of the clitoris is a delicate, but rewarding, activity. The man must ensure that he always touches it with the greatest delicacy but, within the limits of such gentleness, he should roll it between thumb and forefinger, stroke it up and down, and gently excite the tip. In other words he should treat it as he would like his penis to be handled. for that is what the clitoris is: a miniature (and in some women, a not so miniature) feminine penis. He should also ensure that it is adequately lubricated and, if he does not find that sufficient lubrication has reached the clitoris when he touches it, he should damp his finger in the secretions moistening the vaginal lips and spread a film of the mucus on the clitoris: this heightens its sensitivity and protects it from the irritation of dry caresses. We would like to mention that some women like the special stimulation of caresses on a dry clitoris, but most women prefer it to be handled only when it is adequately lubricated.

Having reached this stage, the woman can do what she and the man have been longing for: she should reach her hand down and, lightly, stroke the erect phallus of her man. We repeat that her strokes should be light and that she should resist all temptation to grasp the organ and excite it further. Gentle stroking, far from adding to the sexual pressure of the male, relieves it to an appreciable extent and further aids him to prolong the love play without getting an overwhelming desire to ejaculate. The woman should stroke the upper surface of the phallus, starting from the head and moving down to the base, and then reversing her movement. She should not, on any account, touch the lower surface of the penis, nor should she encircle the organ as if she was going to masturbate the man. Her strokings should be light, a mere trailing of her fingers over the hard, warm, upper surface of the organ. When she finds that the penis is becoming covered with a thin film of secretion... the precoital fluid which is primarily a lubricating liquid... she and the man should, at long last, attempt intercourse.

Dr. William H. Masters and Mrs. Virginia E. Johnson, as a result of the pioneering experiments in their Reproductive Biology Research Foundation in St. Louis, recommend that in cases of premature ejaculation, the experienced woman should assume the woman superior position for the first controlled act of intercourse. Without in any way disputing the findings recorded in **Human Sexual Inadequacy,** we would like to make it clear that the definition of premature ejaculation, as far as Tantric Sex is concerned, is very different from that given by Masters and Johnson. We do not seek to cure the man who has his orgasm before his partner's: such treatment is far beyond the scope of this book. We start with the man who can retain his orgasm for five or ten minutes after insertion, a very acceptable period from western experience. Starting with such a person, who would generally be considered normal, if not gifted with virility, we try to increase his sexual staying power to thirty minutes, perhaps an hour and a half. Thus, our recommendations for intercourse positions are not in conflict with those of Masters and Johnson, but complementary to them.

Nevertheless, in spite of the fact that the orgasmic control problems of our readers are not the same as those faced by the patients of Masters and Johnson, we do agree with the St. Louis researchers that the, so called, 'missionary position' of intercourse is not the right one for the establishment of orgasmic control. The man-lying-on-the-woman position places too much stress on both parties and will destroy the gains already made. We, therefore, recommend the Side Lying or Lateral Position. To achieve sexual connection in this position the male should draw up his leg on the side on which he is lying till it is almost at right angles to his body. The female then places her lower leg, the one that is most in contact with the bed, on the male's drawn up leg, and her upper leg over his upper leg. The man's lower arm should be passed under his partner's neck or shoulders and he should pull her to him so that, eventually, he is lying partially on his back and partially on his side and she, similarly, is lying partially on her side and partially on her front, her breasts resting against the man's chest. The upper arms of both are free to control the movements of each other's bodies... drawing nearer or pushing away... and to caress each other's genital organs and other erogenous zones. When the bodies have been drawn together, the man should search for his partner's clitoris and find the tiny pocket of folded flesh in which it lies: this pocket is formed by the junction of the genital lips of the woman. Having found it he should very gently, place the head of his erect phallus in this moist, enclosing, socket and let it rest there without movement.

We have often been asked why we recommend this unusual position when the vagina is available and ready to welcome the thrusting penis. It is because the vagina is so eager to receive the penis that we suggest this intermediate stage. After prolonged excitation it is extremely likely that, at the first insertion of the penis, vaginal contractions will set in quite involuntarily. If this happens, the stimulus on the penis will be so great that there will be little chance of re-establishing orgasmic control. If, however, the head of the penis is sheltered and, to a certain extent, clasped in the ante-chamber of the clitoris, a sense of accomplishment sweeps over the two partners and, after five or ten minutes, the urge for intromission subsides sufficiently to ensure that there will be no involuntary vaginal contractions on the introduction of the penis.

And that is exactly what is done at this stage,

The male partner withdraws his penis from the clitorine socket and, again very gently and very slowly, slides it into the warm and welcoming vagina; but not more than three centimeters of the penis should be inserted at first. This is an extremely difficult discipline as both the man and the woman will have been sufficiently aroused to want to rush to an orgasm, but they must exercise the greatest control. It helps considerably if both partners

T—6

refrain, strictly, from any other sexual stimulation while the penis is first inserted in the vagina: no fondling, no caressing, no kissing. Lie together and feel the closeness of each other. Breathe deeply to help restore control. Then, after about two minutes of this, the male should withdraw his penis till only the head is touching the vulva. Again a rest of two minutes and deep breathing. Once more insertion for three centimeters, no more, followed by rest in that position and deep breathing by both partners. When this procedure has been continued for fifteen minutes both the male and the female will have become very eager to complete the prolonged act of intercourse. The man should now make a number of shallow, fairly rapid, strokes until he feels the woman digging her fingers into his back and tightening her leg over his. This is her sign that her orgasm is near The man should then give himself over to deep vaginal thrusts and release his orgasm, clutching his satisfied woman to him closely.

By this discipline the male has learnt to withhold his orgasm for more than fifteen minutes after insertion in the female's vagina. This is a considerable gain and one that gives great confidence. It is, however, only the beginning.

At the next sexual encounter the two partners should assume the same lateral position but this time the man should insert his penis for half its length into the vagina. The concentration now, however, is on the slowness and deliberation of his movements. Each stroke, in and out, should take not less than three minutes, longer if possible without losing desire. This calls for considerable control on the part of both partners and the vagina should be copiously lubricated; thus, this can only be achieved after prolonged love play as described in this chapter. If, at any time, the man feels the approach of orgasm, he must withdraw his penis **slowly,** breathing deeply and regularly all the time, and place the head of his organ in the clitorine socket, or even out of total contact with the woman. Deep breathing and removal from contact with the highly stimulating environment of the vagina should enable the man to re-establish control of his orgasmic process within two to three minutes. He can then re-insert his penis for the same three-minute strokes for only half its length. The two essential features of this discipline are that the penis should not be inserted for more than half its length, and the strokes should last for · three minutes or more.

Again, after fifteen or twenty minutes of these controlled movements, the partners may proceed to normal orgasm by the shallow thrusting followed by deep thrusts when the female's orgasm is imminent.

Here the male should use the pelvic exercises we have recommended in an earlier chapter. You will recall that we had advised the male Tantrist to practice the raising and lowering of his penis by means of the muscles in his pelvic region: imagine that he is holding in a full bladder or an urgent bowel movement. The muscles used in these exercises are the ones which control the ejaculatory process. Instinctively, when a man wishes to control his orgasm he tightens these muscles... and thereby hastens the very process he wishes to control! Any tightening o. these muscles leads to a tingling sensation at the base o. the penis and this is a sure sign that ejaculation is due and can only be prevented if erotic stimulation is suspended. When the tingling sensation starts, the man should cease all movement, breathe deeply a number of times and try, consciously, to loosen the buttock muscles. If this is done in time, the sensation will abate and he can continue with his controlled thrusts till the tingling warns him again, when again he must stop, breathe deeply, and relax his muscles. And so on for as long as is required. The more often this is done the easier it becomes to control the orgasmic response.

But to get back to the system of graduated insertions. Still in the lateral position, the male partner should make every fourth insertion a complete one. He should still move slowly and with great deliberation, breathing deeply to maintain his control. When he is certain that he can control his orgasm in spite of the deep insertions into the vagina of his female partner, he can make every third insertion a deep one, and so on till all the thrusts of his penis are for the full length.

It is at this stage that we recommend the favoured Masters and Johnson position for coital control: the Female Superior Position. We suggest that the position be accomplished in a graceful manner from the earlier, the lateral, position. In other words, the male should insert his penis in the female and then he should roll over on to his back pulling the woman on top of him, without breaking sexual contact. The woman should now get into a comfortable 'kneeling' position, her legs straddling his hips. The man's hands should be on her buttocks, particularly when he wants to indicate to her to move faster, slower, or to cease movement altogether. There are many additional advantages to this position: the woman is free to dictate the pace of the intercourse, she feels dominant, she exposes her whole body for caresses, she is relieved of the man's weight. Again, however, the movement should be slow and controlled and, for the first time, the woman can use her internal muscles to squeeze and release the man's sheathed penis and to perfect the exquisite 'milking' motion. But even in this she must always be conscious of, the man's control of his orgasm: she should watch his face closely for signs of approaching ejaculation and pay attention to the pressure of his hands on her hips. This position calls for the greatest understanding and co-ordination of movement between the two partners and the woman can feel a true participator in the man's efforts to reach the highest standards of Tantric virility. Coupling in this position should last for at least twenty minutes, preferably for half an hour, before the woman can signal that she wishes to have an orgasm. The orgasm should be brought about by the movements of the woman, raising and lowering herself on the man's penis... a squatting position is usually best for this... but the woman should be careful that in her enthusiasm she does not completely unsheath herself from the penis. If she does, she should be extra careful to have it re-inserted on her down stroke, for if the tumescent phallus should miss the vaginal cleft the entire weight of the woman might descend on it hurting it badly. This position should also be utilised by the

partners to acquire a variety of coital movements and
sexual co-ordination, bringing into play the muscles developed during the sexual exercises recommended by us
earlier.

A particularly effective coital movement... and one
reputedly specialised in by the women of the southern
states of India... is the hip rotation, much like the old-
time stripper's 'Grind'. This can be done by the man
when he is lying on his back by the simple exercise of
tightening his gleutus maximus muscles, the large muscles of the buttocks, and elevating his hips. After he
has done this for a few times he should then also impart
a slight 'hula-hoop' movement of his hips on the upward and downward thrusts. The corkscrew-like movement of his penis during the upward thrust has a special delight all its own because it lets the phallus touch
every part of the vagina with a particularly demanding
vigor. The female partner should watch this movement
carefully; she will find it far easier to practice it than
the male does because of the natural rotary movement
of the heavier feminine hips. Later, when she assumes
the Female Inferior Position, that is when she is lying
on her back, she should couple the downward corkscrew
movement with a tightening and 'milking' action of her
vaginal muscles. The combined effect of these three
actions... the rotation, the in-and-out motion, and the
'milking' squeeze... provide a sexual stimulus that is
quite indescribable.

Having participated in the Female Superior Position
and retained his orgasmic control the male is ready for
the Rear Entry Position. We recommend that the rear
entry should be effected in the lateral position, that is
with both the partners lying on their sides and facing in
the same direction, the woman in front of the man. The
woman should place a small pillow under her buttocks
and draw up her legs slightly. Her upper body should
be angled slightly away from that of the man so that the
man's upper body and her's forms a V with the junction
at their genital organs. If the couple are lying on their
right sides, the man should place his left thigh over her
left thigh, his right arm under her body to caress her

breasts, and his left arm over her body to caress her clitoris. The insertion of the penis should be done very slowly and there should be no movement till the penis has been completely inserted in the vagina. Even when full insertion has been effected, this position does not allow for considerable movement and the male should restrict himself to a motion of about 10 cm. Considerable advantage can however, be obtained from this position because although there is complete body-to-body contact, the breasts and the clitoris are completely accessible to caressing thereby heightening the erotic stimulation of both the partners in an unusual way. As it is possible that the clitoris will not be sufficiently lubricated for the extensive manipulation permissible in this position we recommend that the fingers caressing the clitoris should be moistened with the male's saliva and the saliva should then be spread on the clitoris. Once again we advise that the intercourse be maintained for as long as possible and, in this position, it should not be difficult to keep the penis erect, and moving, in the vagina for half an hour or more. The man should now have got sufficient experience, and confidence, in the retention of his orgasm and he should be able to give his woman a satisfying orgasm before giving way to his own

Finally, after orgasmic control has been achieved in the earlier positions, the partners are ready for the face-to-face Male Superior Position.

Start with insertion in the face-to-face lateral position. When the initial excitement has been controlled, the male should roll over, very carefully, both partners adjusting their limbs, till the woman is lying on her back and the man is lying between her drawn up and parted legs. A pillow under her buttocks will raise her pelvic region and enable the man to enter her while supporting his weight on either his elbows or hands, and knees. This is the typical male dominating position and as our society places considerable erotic value on it, it is most likely that the erotic stimulation of this position will tend to make the man lose orgasmic control. The man should, consequently, proceed with great caution using all the techniques he has learnt earlier: quarter strokes, follow-

ed by half-strokes, three-quarter strokes and only lastly
venturing into the deep vaginal thrusts. Stroke variations could also be attempted as three shallow strokes
followed by a deep thrust followed by a pause; or two
deep strokes, a pause, four shallow ones, a pause; etc.
The woman should also be encouraged to gradual parti-
cipation, starting from a rotary motion and moving up
to an up-and-down movement, to full response and co-
ordination with her partner's thrusts. It is, however,
essential, that intercourse in this position should never
last less than ½ an hour, and that insertion and controlled movement for an hour should be frequently sustained. With the discipline that has been given by the earlier
positions, an hour-long intercourse should not be difficult
to achieve without conscious effort.

In fact, one of the greatest physical rewards of Tantra
is that after an exquisite hour-long intercourse, the orgasm
is so explosive and complete that both partners fall into
a post-orgasmic stupor from which they emerge extremely refreshed and invigorated and ready to tackle all the
problems of the day, but always looking forward to their
next ecstatic bout of sustained Tantric Sex.

We shall, in the next chapter, briefly consider a number of intercourse positions. Knowledge of these positions will give considerable variety to your regimen of
Tantric Sex.

Chapter Thirteen

Positions for Variety

We have, in the last chapter, suggested a few intercourse positions for the specific purpose of teaching a man how to gain orgasmic control. The positions could, of course, also be used to give variety to the sexual life and, once the early orgasm problems have been settled, we expect them to be used for this valuable purpose. Monotony in sex, and particularly in Tantric Sex, is dangerous, because it leads to boredom and makes sex a mechanical exercise. And yet it is surprising how many couples restrict themselves to a few conventional positions after the heady honeymoon.

Tantric partners are on an endless honeymoon and so they should be able to make full use of the seed-ideas offered in this chapter. Many couples seem to believe that once the penis has been introduced into the vagina, they should stay in that position till orgasm. This, it would appear, is a western influenced belief: because the orgasm occurs so soon after intromission there is little time to savour a variety of positions and thrusts. If a Tantric couple subscribes to the same belief their sex life is bound to become monotonous very soon. We doubt, however, if they will be able to maintain one position throughout their prolonged sexual engagement: even a slight change in the relative positions of the two bodies is enough to vary the sensations experienced. We advise you to study the positions we give below so that you will be able to appreciate how the use of a cushion, or a realignment of the legs, lets you and your partner adjust from one stance to another so that there is little change in the rhythm of the act, and hardly any interruption.

We shall start with the **Woman Supine** position, the so-called Missionary Position... a name allegedly given by amused South Sea Islanders who wondered at the monotony with which their missionaries persisted in using only this position: they felt it had some mystical cultural significance. In a way, they were right, as we now know. In this position, the woman lies on her back and the man stretches out above her, his penis entering her vagina through her bent and parted legs. The man should support himself on his elbows and knees.

As an interesting variation to this position, the man should ask the woman to draw back her legs till her knees are near her ears. This raises up the vulva and gives a depth of penetration that is difficult to achieve in any other position. Unless she is very flexible, the woman will have to hold her legs with her hands and it is likely that she will begin to feel suffocated after a short while because of the pressure on her abdomen consequently this position should not be held for very long. It is also not advisable to get into this position after a heavy meal. As can be appreciated, the man will have to crouch into order to maintain contact in this position, but the depth of penetration gives a certain feeling of closeness that makes this position worth trying, if only for a short while.

From this position it is easy to move into the next one when the woman places her legs on the man's shoulders. There is still a certain pressure on the woman's abdomen, but it is much less than the pressure experienced in the last position. The man will, in all likelihood, have to raise himself to his hands, or rather, he will have to now support himself on his hands rather than on his elbows. Because the woman's thighs exert a counter-pressure on the man's shoulders the movements in this position have a spring-like quality about them and makes it particularly attractive for short durations. This effect is enhanced if the man supports himself only on his hands and toes, his body positioned at a straight incline over hers and making contact with the woman's body only at the genitals. This sub-variation, however, puts a considerable strain on the man's stomach and pelvic muscles and, unless he is trim and fit, he is likely to feel sore in this region the next day.

Lowering her legs still further, the woman should now cross them over the man's hips thereby using her powerful leg muscles to lock the sexual embrace. The vagina is shortened and the man's penis is likely to touch the cervix. Naturally, movements in this position are restricted and, therefore, it helps to retain the orgasm. The entire movements of the partners, in this position, is centered around the pelvic region and is effective when the muscles of this area have been developed as suggested by us earlier.

Another position for prolongation calls for the woman to lock her ankles over those of her partner and to draw him to her embracing his back with her arms. There is a great feeling of closeness in this position and virtually no pelvic movement. The woman can, however, make full use of her vaginal muscles and we have known men to be brought to orgasm by this means. It is possible, however, to get a certain amount of lateral motion into the act and, if this is coupled with the contraction of the vaginal muscles, the resulting orgasms are extremely satisfying. The vagina and the clitoris are considerably stimulated by such movements.

In all the positions already described, the man's legs have been placed inside the woman's. Excellent variations of sensations can also be obtained when the position of the legs is reversed: when the man's legs are placed outside those of his female partner.

It is possible to have intercourse with the man's knees on two sides of his partners and her legs stretched straight. We recommend that you attempt this merely because it provides a slight variation but it has little to add to the sensations offered by any of the other positions. Penetration is not deep and there is every likelihood of the penis becoming unsheated from the vagina. Most couples find that it provides little satisfaction in spite of the fact that the clitoris is stimulated for almost the entire length of the penis. It also shares a disadvantage with the last position in that the woman has to bear the entire weight of her male partner: unless she embraces him closely they are likely to lose genital contact.

The vaginal clasp on the penis is enhanced, however, if the woman crosses her legs at knee level after intromission of the penis. As we have said earlier, the man's legs should be outside those of his partner's. In this position, the closed vaginal walls of the female tighten around the base of the penis, restricting movement but ensuring the closest possible contact between the penis and the vagina. It is also likely that the penis will remain hard for some considerable time after orgasm because the flow of blood, away from the penis, is hindered by the enfolding vagina. We recommend, however, that the woman should not make use of this post-orgasmic turgidity in order to work herself to another orgasm: the penis is particularly sensitive after orgasm and further movements of the vagina will be resented by the man until he has been able to raise the level of his desire again. The clasping and releasing of the vaginal muscles may be indulged in as this motion does not hurt the sensitive penis after its orgasm. If the woman can achieve her own orgasm by this internal motion she should feel free to do so. It is also likely that her ecstasy will spark a sympathetic response from her man and make him get his 'second wind' sooner than normal.

If the man wishes to intensify the contact between himself and his partner in this position he could pass his legs under the crossed legs of his partner and lock them tightly.

The angle of the vagina, relevant to the penis, can also be varied by using the small cushions we had proposed when listing the 'equipment' for your Tantric Room.

In any of the Woman Supine positions, if a hard cushion is placed under her pelvic region... roughly between the small of the back and base of the spine.. this makes the vagina curve downwards and outwards. Intercourse in this position brings the penis in contact with the clitoris and allows for deep penetration.

Similarly, if the same cushion is now moved below the woman's buttocks, the angle of her vagina is altered as it curves upwards and inwards, making the vaginal passage lie at roughly the same angle as the penis. This, naturally, leads to a satisfyingly deep penetration and, consequently, an intense orgasm. We particularly re commend this position if the woman is inclined to have a large stomach, or the man is self-conscious about the shortness of his penis. In passing we would, however, like to say that the vagina is such a flexible organ, and the positions of intercourse so varied, that the length of a man's penis should make no difference to the quality of the intercourse. What does matter, of course, is the amount of confidence he has in his own virility. If he lacks confidence, believing that his inadequate penis is likely to be resented by the woman, we recommend that he concentrate on the positions in which the woman draws up her legs and thus shortens the length of her vaginal passage. Intercourse in such positions is likely to restore his self-esteem and lead to a satisfactory intercourse in any position which later, might take his, or his partner's fancy.

We have already dealt with two **Lateral Positions** in the last chapter. We would now like you to consider the variations on this position because they are the easiest change to make from the Woman Supine position.

The woman lies on her side and draws up her legs so that her thighs are at right-angles to her body. The man lies on his side behind her, in the position described in the last chapter, and inserts his penis. If the woman has large hips a hard cushion under the man's hip will help raise him for genital contact. Similarly, if the woman is appreciably slimmer than the man, the cushion should be placed under her hip to give the right compensation. The grasp of the vagina on the penis can be varied by the man inserting his legs between those of the woman, thereby easing the hold of the vaginal walls, or by him embracing her legs with his in which case the clutch of the vagina on the penis is tightened.

A variation of this position gives a very restful intercourse, with the minimum of movement. The woman should lie on her back and draw up her legs as in the first Woman Supine position. The man then lies on his side and inserts his legs under the arch formed by her nearer leg. The woman then lowers her far leg and the man places his lower leg... the one in contact with the bed... under the far leg of the woman, and his upper leg over her far leg. Thus, if the man is lying on her right, his right leg is over both of his and her left is over his left leg and under his right; her left leg being held in the pincer of his legs. Their genitals should now be in contact and his penis should easily slide into her vagina. The interlacing of their legs ensures that the genital contact will be maintained. This position is extremely relaxing for the woman, almost as relaxing for the man, and is particularly recommended for a post-orgasmic contact if the couple wish to Float after orgasm. Most couples find it convenient to fall asleep in this position and awake with a feeling of great closeness even though their bodies might have separated during the normal movements of sleep.

If, after the last position, there is still a desire for intercourse, there will be no difficulty to move from this position to all the variations of the **Man Supine** position. All the woman has to do is to raise her trunk, while the man shifts his weight from his side to his back. By the time the man is flat on his back the woman should have swung her left leg over his hips and be straddling him without their genitals having lost their connection. As we have said earlier, all the movements of intercourse should be done with grace and co-ordination and there is a particular satisfaction in moving from one position to another without having to withdraw the penis from the vagina, with the minimum of movements and with the greatest harmony between the couple.

On completion of the movement, the woman should be kneeling with her legs on both sides of her man. From now on she can take a dominant role in the intercourse: this has a particularly erotic effect on both the man and woman, particularly if they come from a society where the male is still considered the dominant sex.

Couples normally use the female dominant position we have described....along with its variation....in the last chapter: the one in which the woman kneels over her partner. Other variations, however, could be as interesting.

A position which duplicates the 'missionary position' calls for the man to lie on his back with his legs drawn up at the knees and his feet resting on the bed. The woman comes over him, between his thighs, supporting herself on her knees and hands. She lowers her pelvis to receive his penis into her and, when the penetration is complete, she stretches out and lies on top of him.

As a variation to this position she could cross her legs at the knees in order to imprison his penis and then use her internal muscles to squeeze and release his tightly-held penis.

Alternatively, she could kneel with her legs on two sides of his hips, in the original position, and bend forward so that she can kiss and caress the man.

A more difficult variation, but often illustrated in Tantric literature, is when the bodies of the partners duplicate the position of an open book. It can be effected through either the male of female dominant positions and through another interesting sub-variation.

After intromission has been made, with either of the partners lying supine....it is easiest when the female is in the dominant position....the female places her feet behind the male's head by stretching her legs along his upper body and over his shoulders. In this position her upper body should, of course, be raised at 90 degrees to the supine male. This is a most relaxing position because the male, his head resting on the females feet, is able to see his dominant partner and she is able to see him. The movements in this position are made by the male tightening and relaxing his buttocks giving a springy bounce to his woman. The tension in both the bodies gives the partners a sense of great fitness.

From this position, the woman gradually lowers her body backwards till it is lying between her partner's spread feet. In the final position, as we have already described, the partners' bodies resemble an open book joined by their genital organs. Erection can be sustained in this position for a long time and this is another position suitable for post-orgasmic Floating.

After doing the Open-book position the partners

should have no difficulty in changing to the **Sitting Positions.**

Sitting up from the Open-book Position, you and your partner hold hands and draw yourselves up, adjusting your legs so that the woman's legs are slightly drawn up with her feet resting on the bed on two sides of the man's hips. Her legs will cross over the man's thighs, her arms will be around his neck. The man also draws his legs up in the same way, placing his feet on the bed on two sides of his partners hips, his arms around her back. If the sexual connection has not been broken... and only a little care is needed to retain contact.... you are now sitting on the bed facing each other, holding each other with your hands, supporting with your legs. Now, very slowly and rhythmically, begin to sway backwards and forwards. With a little practice you should be able to sway fairly far backwards and forwards giving a delightful motion to your coupled genital organs. This is a fun position and the couple must be very serious minded indeed to refrain from breaking out in laughter before they've done this for five minutes. The fun of it probably delays orgasm because when you allow yourselves to think of the stimulation your genital organs are receiving you will realise that the sensation is intense and varied. If you decide to have an orgasm in this position it is best for the man to draw the woman close to him, so that their bodies are in contact and she is sitting on his lap, his penis deeply penetrating her, their arms holding them close when they reach their climax.

For those who wish to take their sex more seriously, Tantric illustrations popularise a similar position with the couples facing each other, sitting, her legs on two sides on his hips, his legs folded around her buttocks, their upper bodies in close physical contact. This is another position for delaying orgasm and is very effective for Floating. The movements in this posture are, naturally, restricted.

Other sitting positions make use of the chairs we have recommended for your Tantric Room. We recommend that you do these in front of a mirror because the sight of you and your partner reflected in the illuminated glass adds a new dimension to your sexual stimulus.

The usual sitting position calls for the man to sit in the armless chair and take the woman on his lap, facing him, her legs straddling his hips. If the woman holds the man tightly, they can both co-ordinate their movements while he can fondle her breasts and kiss them. It will be difficult for him to caress her clitoris because the contact between the bodies....particularly between their abdomens....is normally to close to permit the insertion of a hand.

The reverse position has the woman sitting on the mans lap, but facing outwards. She will have to lean her upper body outwards slightly because if she leans too close to him the man's penis is likely to lose contact. There are, however, a number of advantages to this position. For one thing, both the partners can see each other's reactions in the mirror: the woman find it particularly stimulating to watch her own reflection as the man's hands squeeze and milk her breasts and caress her nipples. If the woman leans back slightly the man has access to her clitoris and, here again, the woman has a clear view of this erect little organ being lovingly teased. Finally, if they are using the low chair we have suggested for the Tantric Room, the woman's feet will be on the ground giving her support and allowing her to move as she likes.

Another interesting variation of the sitting position is for the man to sit on the floor facing his partner, his legs stretched under the chair in which she is sitting. He then reaches out to her and slides her off the chair carefully, and on to his erect penis. The woman can lean back on the chair and, supporting herself on her hands or elbows, raise and lower herself to a mutual orgasm.

The last position, though classified by us as a sitting one can also be categorised as a **Leaning Position**. We recommend only two variations of this group because they are apt to be rather strenuous and physically strenuous sex has little place in Tantra except to offer a change of pace, occasionally.

The classic leaning position is when the woman sits

on the edge of the bed with her legs dangling over the side, and the man stands in front of her and slides his penis into her vagina. If the bed has not been made to the height recommended by us it will probably be necessary for the woman to raise herself by sitting on a firm cushion. There is a certain wanton pleasure in this position because the woman leans on her arms and obviously thrusts out her genitals for her partner. There are not many advantages for the man, however, because he is liable to get an orgasm whilst standing on his feet and that is not generally appreciated by most males.

It helps if the woman, after sexual contact has been made, wraps her legs around the man's hips and clasps him with her arms. The closeness and depth of penetration of this position seems to compensate for the disadvantages of the man having to stand.

Athletic men, or the normal man who is feeling particularly fit, might like to move from the last position to the classic Yab-Yum position of Tantric iconography. Most Tantric deities, ...particularly in Tibetan and other Himalayan Tantra.....are depicted in close sexual embrace with their Shaktis in the Yab-Yum stance. This stance effectively indicates the power of sex, the strength of the union, and the dependance of the male principle on the female and vice versa. If you and your partner wish to try this position, you should make sexual contact on the edge of the bed as described above and then, when the female partner has wrapped her arms and legs around the male, the man should place his hands under her buttocks and then move back from the bed. The most striking feature of this position is the woman's sense of complete surrender to the man, and the man's of protectiveness and virility towards the woman wrapped around him. Penetration is deep but movements are restricted and we do not recommend that this position should be held for long.

The **Rear Entry Positions** also give a very strong feeling of primitive sexuality, possibly because they most closely resemble the coupling of animals and evoke an ancient racial memory.

The simplest rear entry position has the woman

kneeling on the bed on her hands and knees, as close to the edge as possible. The man, standing on the floor behind her, enters her and then leans his body slightly forward, caressing her breasts and clitoris. Movement is unrestricted and this is a position that becomes particularly effective if done before a mirror.

A variation of this position can be had by the woman kneeling in the centre of the bed, her body sharply inclined forward, resting her head on her folded arms on the bed. This stance thrusts up her vagina and allows the man's penis to enter it with ease even though he is kneeling upright behind her. Great vigor can be given to his thrusts if he holds her by her hips and urges himself into her. The partners should be warned that when the man removes his penis from the woman's vagina in this position her vagina might emit a sound because of the escaping air. Once the partners get used to this phenomenon the sound can assume an erotic impact but if they are not expecting it, it is likely to put them off this very stimulating position for a while. If the woman does not wish to rest her head on the bed, she can use the bolster, or large columnar pillow, to support her head and arms.

The bolster can also be used to support the back in any of the positions if the partner lying down wishes to raise the body slightly, or to vary the angle of the sexual encounter.

Rear entry intercourse can also be performed by the male lying on the prone body of the female provided a cushion is used to elevate the woman's organs suitably. Such elevation is particularly necessary if the woman has well padded buttocks.

These are a few of the basic positions of intercourse and they should serve as a take-off point for the imagination to devise many others, with the co-operation of your willing partner. There is no need, whatsoever, to restrict your love play or intercourse to the Tantric Room: a variety of locations is bound to lead to a variety of positions. Intercourse in a sunken bath is particularly appealing because the water buoys up both bodies and the feel of wet limbs and organs adds to the sensation experienced. It is for this reason that we have recommended that a sunken hand rail should be installed all round the bath. With the rail for support there is virtually no position of intercourse that can not be accomplished in cool, or blood-heat, water.

As an example of the extent to which eastern lovers were prepared to go to bring variety into their sex life, we would like to quote from that Arabian classic of erotics, **The Perfumed Garden** of Sheik Nefzawi.

The man secures the hands and feet of a willing woman in the region of her neck so that, in appearance, she looks like one of those idols displayed by the Greeks, or else as in the posture known as the Bow assumed by various Indian savants. In effect her Most Feminine part is thrust outwards like the dome of the palace of a great king. Others have compared it to a pomegranate split open by the force of its own ripe juices. Having affixed her thus he then passes soft, supporting cloths around her body as trusses (taking care not to hurt her or mar the unbroken beauty of her skin). These trusses he binds to a strong rope passing through a pulley firmly adhered to the ceiling of the bedchamber. Having done so he stretches himself below and, drawing on the rope in his hand, raised the woman upwards. Now, with a male sexual part on him worthy of the title of Extinguisher of Passions, the man proceeds to lower the woman upon his indomitable weapon till it is sheathed like a Damascus sword. Whereupon he withdraws the weapon by elevating the woman thus revealing the true honed gleam on his piercer, eagerly awaiting the next thrust. Similarly he raises and lowers the woman till the pleasure-war is ended and that which gushes forth is not blood but no less worthy than blood and the cries of the 'dying' rend the perfumed air.

While we do not expect to see pulleys and harnesses in the Tantric Rooms of our readers, we expect we have made our point: Variety is the Spice of the Sex Life of Tantra. If you ring the changes in positions and techniques, you will not need to ring the changes in partners.

But that is a subject that we shall, more fully, deal with in the next....and last....chapter of this book

Part V

TANTRIC MORALITY

Part V

TANTRIC MORALITY

Chapter Fourteen

Tantra and Morality

Is Tantra immoral? That is a question you will have
to answer before you bring this book into your house.
And more important than your answer is your actions:
what do you intend to do with the book? Do you intend
to hide it from your more conservative friends and
relatives? Or do you propose to flaunt it as a symbol
of your sexual emancipation? If you answer 'Yes' to
either question, you do believe that Tantra is immoral,
or certainly that it is not quite respectable.

Well, if it is any consolation to you, you are in the
majority. Most people in India, where they should know
better, think that Tantra is a dark and suspect science:
all very well for the idle rich and the ignorant but not
the thing for the solid, down-to-earth citizen. In fact,
they are so averse to the entire topic that they would
not like to study it for fear of contamination. Thus,
their opinions are formed, as so many public opinions
are often formed, on an unholy mixture of rumour,
tradition and running-with-the-herd prejudice. The fact
that Tantra is, in some way, connected with sex, further
discredits it in Indian eyes: as if sex were anathema in
India.

If you decide to toe the conventional line we cannot
blame you. There are very few of us who are so independent that we can afford to swim against the current.
We are happy that you have bought this book because,
then, there is a chance that your attitudes will change.
And the more people who view the world through the
eyes of Tantra, the greater are our chances of survival.
For we sincerely believe that in Tantra lies the solution
to most, if not all, the world's problems.

And if you give us the time we should like to tell
you why we think so. We warn you that it will be

a long journey which will take you from morality to government and then to world problems and their solutions and only then to Tantra.

To start with, what is morality? Or, for that matter, what is law or religion? The boundaries between the three are so vague that it is difficult to distinguish where one ends and the other begins. Is divorce a moral, legal or religious question? And in what category would you place questions of abortion, mercy killing, prostitution, apartheid, war and the Bomb? Thus, in any enquiry into the nature and origins of morality we have to treat the three topics as if they were facets of the same subject. For the sake of convenience we shall call this collective subject the Law.

But what is the Law?

A man marooned on a desert island can wake when he likes, sleep when he likes and eat when and what he likes: the choices open to him are restricted only by his own ability, inclinations and the resources of the island. He is not subject to any law. A man living in a tight-knit community, on the other hand, must curb his actions to fit into the laws of that community, or be punished for breaking those laws.

Why then do human beings, who presumably started with an unrestricted freedom of choice, inflict such self-imposed curbs on themselves? Why, in other words, does a free man join a freedom-curbing society? The answer is obvious: men form themselves into societies for mutual protection....protection against the environment, hunger, common enemies, disease or the other hazards which assail a lone man. The lone hunter, forms a hunting party because, alone, he cannot provide adequate food, clothing and shelter for himself. But when he forms a hunting party with others, who were formally lone hunters themselves, he has to surrender some of his untrammelled rights. He has to say "If Oog the Aromatic goes upwind to scare the animals, and Aagh the Fire-carrier lights the dry grass when the animals are running, I, Gor the Mightiest of Bowmen, will slaughter the animals when they rush through the pass." And when the animals have been killed, Oog, Aagh and Gor have to share the spoils. Before he formed the hunting party Gor could eat the best pieces of every animal he killed, but he did not kill many animals. Now, there is no shortage of food, but his right to eat the best pieces is diminished by the rights of Oog and Aagh. And if these three hunters do not agree with the way the spoils have been shared they will fight with each other and the society of the hunting party will fall apart.

Thus, it becomes clear that societies are bound together by counter-balancing rights and obligations between the members of that society.

This, then, is what the law is: the rule made by society for its own protection. And the closer the members of that society adhere to those rules, the stronger that society will be.

Or, to put it in other words, the strength and stability of a society depends on the strength and stability of the empathy between its members.

But a society does not exist in a vacuum: it is very much a part of its environment. With the approach of an Ice Age, for instance, Stone Age tribes had to move out of their old, familiar, territories because the cold was creeping in. This move called for new conventions, new laws: a farming-hunting community had to become a purely hunting community as they moved to new lands with strange soil; a fishing-herding community had to become a purely herding community as they left their old lakes and could find no new ones. All this called for changes that went deep into the fabric of community life. Prosperous farmers who were the former community leaders had now to take second place to skilled hunters, fisher-kings now bowed to shepherd-princes; wheat and fish, the prime barter items, gave way to meat and wool; the stable marriage laws of village life were changed to suit the easier social structure of nomads.

Some communities, of course, did not change fast enough. Their traditions were too rigid, their old men had too much of a say on the community mores. Such communities languished and died.

Thus, the viability of a society depends on the speed with which it can respond to changing circumstances and change the Law governing that society.

In a small society such changes are easily made. Democracy was born in the Greek city states where every citizen could take a direct part in the governing of the community. If you felt strongly about anything you could express your mind in the Forum and if the majority of your fellow citizens shared your views, they voted for your proposal and your proposal became law. Society moved fast in those days because it was small and flexible, and responsive.

But responsive societies survive and grow; and growing societies become large; and large societies are not directly responsive. Government by delegation sets in and delegates, regrettably, make the common, human, mistake of equating their personal welfare with the welfare of the country they claim to serve.

This situation is not unique to any country or any nation: it is a malady which effects all mankind and there seems to be no solution. But there is a solution as we shall find when we specify the gravest problems facing mankind today.

If you ask a group of well-read people to list the world's most serious problems, the chances are that they will include:

> War
> Pollution of the Environment
> The Population Explosion
> The Energy Crisis
> Corruption in Public Life, and
> Permissiveness in Society.

Our views are slightly different. While we do not deny that these are matters of grave concern, we feel that most of them are symptomatic rather than fundamental. We believe that the really basic problems, the ones that can account for all the other ailments of world society, are

The Ecological Balance
The Distribution of World Resources
The Break-up of the Family, and
The Diminishment of Awareness.

Let us take the case of War: essentially an economic problem. Nations go to war because they want room to live and to grow, a greater share of the world's resources. It is so, also, with corruption in public life and the energy crisis: both are basically distribution problems. There are rich nations and poor nations, and rich people and poor people; both realise that the resources available are limited but, in spite of this realisation, both want to get a larger share of these goods and services and if society does not give it they seek to get it by extra-social means. When industry, which includes the vast consumer market, enhances its demands beyond the recycling capacity of nature, pollution sets in. Thus, pollution is also, essentially, a distribution problem: the cars, containers and chemicals that find their way into the American scrap heap would find users in the developing economies and, consequently, would not pollute the earth and upset the ecological balance. The population problem is also the result of the distribution of resources and the break-up of the family. The more of the world's goods a family has, the less children it breeds but the goods of the world are not distributed equitably: one American baby consumes as much as 8 Indian babies! All countries which suffer most from excessive populations were once strongholds of the family: the family provided the means of livelihood and imposed their own population restraints in the form of marriage laws, cohabitation prohibitions and inheritance customs. In Vedic India, for instance, prostitutes held appreciable social status and thus provided an effective safety valve for the sex urge with the least repercussions on society. Older women in the family advised the younger ones on contraceptive and abortive techniques. Disease, itself, took on a religious mantle: smallpox was regarded as the visit of the Goddess. When, however, the influence of the family waned, these restraints were removed and no acceptable ones were imposed. Permissiveness, we need hardly state, is a direct result of the falling status of the family. To this day, the strongly ethnic communities in large cities, all over the world, have the least problems of permissiveness because of the restraining hand of family pressure.

But, at the heart of all the problems in the diminishment of awareness. Most people, certainly all those who are in a position to influence the course of events, know the consequences of their actions. And yet they deliberately opt for the short-sighted view. This is because very few people admit that there is any need to project consequences beyond the span of their own lives. Unconvinced of immortality, uncertain of timeless values such as truth and justice, and unconcerned with the lives of their fellow-men, leaders of society judge everything from the yardstick of their own value. They are neither evil nor, by their own reasoning, impractical. They are just not aware of any other criterion.

Thus, at the epicentre of all the disasters that threaten man, is the root cause: the Diminishment of Awareness.

This is where Tantra provides the solution. It cannot change the system of government but it can change the people who are governed and, through them, society.

To start with, Tantra uses Sex to achieve its aims. Sex is the one currency common to all mankind. Man is, biologically, an over-sexed beast and the urge to copulate often overcomes the urge to survive. "Love", says the old proverb, "laughs at locksmiths". Indeed it does, and also at barbed wire, torture and the possibility of execution as was illustrated time and again when German prisoners risked all this to meet, and love, in the most menacing of environments. Sex, therefore, is the one common ground on which all mankind can meet. Thus, by basing a discipline on sex, Tantra provides a fundamentally empathic foundation in a world woefully short of empathy.

Next, Tantra offers the reward of ecstasy and, apparent, self-indulgence to the highest degree. This is a very important factor because sexual frustration accounts for more social perversions than is normally admitted. Hitler was a sexual incompetent with a frustrated obsession for his niece. Stalin reportedly had his wife murdered. Mussolini had VD and was so protective of his sexual potency that he had a habit of touching his genitals whenever bad news was brought to him. Even Roosevelt, now being classified as a benign tyrant, had a long-sustained, but frustratingly clandestine extra-marital affair: hardly the conduct of a sexually satisfied man. The list could be multiplied almost indefinitely if research, and the law, permitted. Victorian sexual hypocricy and Puritan sexual frigidity must be held responsible for much of the aggression of Britain's colonial out-thrust and the rapacity of American business. The sexual urge is such a primal force that it will find an outlet in unpredictable ways. Tantra prevents sexual frustration.

Third, Tantra offers full sexual expression within the framework of the family.

The family is the basis of all stable societies. This is so because it is the fundamental unit of society. Law, the binding force of society, cannot exist when the individual stands alone. The lone hunter, as we have seen, subjects himself to the Law only when he becomes a member of the society and the smallest unit of society is the family. Thus, laws start with the family and are strongest in those societies where the family is most stable. This is where the so-called revolutionary societies fail: in trying to abolish, or weaken, the family they are virtually abolishing, or weakening their own society. Russia, after flirting with socialist substitutes for the family, has returned to elaborate wedding ceremonies in palatial halls and is increasingly concentrating on consumer goods for Society families. China, for all its much vaunted communes, has again permitted families to live together and bind themselves to their traditional patch of Chinese earth. Fast vanishing are the 'good old days' when a commune official permitted a husband to spend a specified conception-period with his wife, and made a note of the day and time for the breeding records!

Tantra, by providing the greatest sexual variety between husband and wife, strengthens the marriage bond with the cement of constantly renewed sexual attraction. A contented husband and wife have a stable marriage, a stable marriage gives a stable family, and a stable family gives a stable society. Divorce, wife-swapping, and sexual-permissiveness are the symptoms of a shattered family life. To rephrase an old saw, 'The family that loves together, lives together.' The Tantric family are bound by the ties of love and stability because there is absolutely no incentive for the husband and the wife to seek greener pastures in their neighbours' backyards: they know that the greenest pastures lies at home.

Fourthly, Tantra increases awareness.

Tantra hones the senses, increases their receptivity. Tantrics are more aware of what is happening around them than any other group of people. To the Tantric, all creation is a living manifestation of driving sexuality. Tantrics are thus constantly aware of the subtlest nuances of change in the people they meet, the situations they encounter, the scenes that surround them. This awareness gives them a total involvement in all creation. Thus, no true Tantric can ever be guilty of ecological crimes because, to him, the whole of creation is an extension of himself. Like the poet-mystic John Donne, Tantrics believe that

"No man is an Island, entire of itself;
Every man is a piece of the Continent, a piece of
the main."

With this awareness of the whole of creation as a unified entity, Tantrics have no difficulty in appreciating the need to share the world's goods and services to the best advantage of all. To the Tantric, the individual has as much, or as little, right to individuality as has any single cell in his body. And while no man would willingly starve any one of his cells, he is always conscious of the fact that the health of the whole body is of fundamental importance; he will not permit one cell, or even one group of cells, to fatten at the expense of the rest.

Fifthly, Tantra enriches the inner life.

More than half this book is devoted to the mind, and most of the rest is concerned with providing a rich environment for the mind to grow in. Tantra shows its adherents the wonderful worlds that lie in ecstatic experience. This is the vision that young drug addicts... frustrated with the scrabbling materialism of modern society....strive for. This is the vision in which lies authentic non-aggression: not the pacifism of the drop out, but the conquering maturity of Christ, Buddha and the great seers of Hinduism. Tantra, thus, gives the true psychedelic experience sought for by modern youth, without the danger of drugs. It also gives the moral authority that, today, is woefully lacking in society.

Sixthly, Tantra taps the intuition.

The sexual power is the source of all intuition. The intuitive faculty is as real as the talent of logic and it is used in ancient tribal communities such as those of the American Indians. According to Brazilian scholar Felicitas Barreto, a famous Amerindian scholar, when a grave problem confronts the Kaiato tribe, the men

> "...sit motionless in a circle for hours, holding each other by the shoulder as in an endless chain and not saying a word....I know from the women that the men are conversing with heaven."

This gift of gestalt thought is also used, in a crude form, by modern industry in their 'brain storming' sessions but our society is fast losing the ability to tap this inexhaustible reservoir of collective experience. Persons who are naturally creative tap this power, but they do so in an indisciplined way, subject to moods, whims and fancies. Tantra releases intuition in a controlled manner so that a Tantric is always gently creative, but can be intensely creative if the need arises. The system of Floating and problem-solving that we have described in this book are essentially systems to utilise intuition and creativity. Thus traditional Tantric societies....such as those in Assam, Bengal, Kerala, Rajasthan and the Himalayan states, are rich in handicrafts and the arts. True social progress can only be achieved in a society which is responsive to its environment. Creativity drawn from intuition is the most effective way to establish and encourage such sensitivity.

Finally, and this is the most important of all, Tantra develops empathy.

The final object of Tantra is empathy: empathy with the world of nature, empathy with the Tantric partner, empathy with the source of all creation. So real is the empathy of a Tantrist that western Tantrists, innured to the non-contact, non-demonstrative, social customs of their society, get startled at their own reactions after undergoing Tantric sexual disciplines in the privacy of their own homes and with their marriage mates. Suddenly, when they are in public places, they are almost overcome with empathy for their less fortunate fellows. One Tantrist, whilst travelling in a public transport, could not resist an empathic urge to succour a total stranger because the stranger seemed overwhelmed by her personal problems. He introduced himself and spoke to her with such love and understanding that soon she poured out her heart to him. Years later he learnt that he had saved her life by turning her aside from the final immorality of suicide.

Thus Tantra gives empathy, and empathy gives awareness and awareness strikes at the root of the problem of world morality. Or lack of it.

Which brings us to the end of this book. We hope you have liked it and found it useful. But remember that when you have mastered all we have written in this book you will only have crossed the threshold of Tantra. A whole new world of experience, and power and ecstasy, lies before you. Embrace it with unrestrained joy for that, in the last analysis, is the way of Tantra.

And may Joy be your ecstatic companion in the wonderful journey ahead......